OTHER FOLKLORE BOOKS
BY M. A. JAGENDORF

American Folklore Series

NEW ENGLAND BEAN POT

UPSTATE, DOWNSTATE:
Folk Stories of the Middle Atlantic States

SAND IN THE BAG:
And Other Stories of Ohio, Indiana, and Illinois

THE MARVELOUS ADVENTURES OF JOHNNY DARLING

European Folk-Stories Series

THE MERRY MEN OF GOTHAM

TYLL ULENSPIEGEL'S MERRY PRANKS

THE PRICELESS CATS
And Other Italian Folk Stories

THE GYPSIES' FIDDLE
And Other Gypsy Stories (with C. H. Tillhagen)

IN THE DAYS OF THE HAN
From Ancient Chinese Legends

PIERRE PATELIN

DOCTORS ALL

BY M. A. JAGENDORF

with illustrations by Shane Miller

NOODLEHEAD
STORIES

from around the world

THE
VANGUARD
PRESS
NEW
YORK

Second Printing

To Fred Crumb

WHOSE LAUGHTER CREATES THE GOOD THINGS OF LIFE

Acknowledgment and Thanks

It would take too many pages to name all the persons who told me these tales—all the many kinds of persons in so many parts of the world. Some of their names are in the notes, but I thank them all, named and unnamed.

Special thanks are due to Evan Esar, who knows more about humor and its history and value than anyone I know. Ben Botkin and Bertha Nathan also gave me some valuable suggestions.

Thanks are also due to the editors of *Jack and Jill,* that excellent magazine for young children, in which the Turkish tale, "The Wisdom of the Lord," was first published.

M. A. J.

CONTENTS

Plant a Story—Reap a Story:

A Storyteller's Introduction 13

1. The Horse-Egg *(India)* 19
2. Don't Marry Two Wives *(India)* 24
3. The Noodlehead Tiger *(India)* 30
4. There Are Such People *(India)* 34
5. Do You Know? *(Greece)* 37
6. The Donkey of Abdera *(Greece)* 40
7. Barefoot in Bed *(Greece)* 43
8. The Fox in the Hole *(Jewish)* 45
9. The Golden Shoes *(Jewish)* 48
10. The Great Traveler of Chelm *(Jewish)* 53
11. Figs for Gold, Figs for Folly *(Jewish)* 59
12. Donkeys All *(Syria)* 63

13. The Cow and the Thread *(Arabia)*   *68*

14. Ceylon Sillies *(Ceylon)*   *72*

15. Like Master, Like Servant *(China)*   *75*

16. The Sad Victory *(China)*   *78*

17. When Noodlehead Marries Noodlehead *(Africa)*   *85*

18. The Foolish Lion and the Silly Rooster *(Africa)*   *89*

19. Who Is Who? *(Persia)*   *93*

20. Magic! Silly Magic! *(Japan)*   *97*

21. The Farmer's Secret *(Japan)*   *100*

22. The Wisdom of the Lord *(Turkey)*   *102*

23. The Costly Feast *(Turkey)*   *105*

24. The Flying Fool *(South America)*   *111*

25. The Wise Men of Gotham *(England)*   *115*

26. The Brave Men of Austwick *(England)*   *119*

27. Knucklehead John *(England)*   *122*

28. A Sheep Can Only Bleat *(Scotland)*   *127*

29. A New Way to Boil Eggs *(Ireland)*   *130*

30. The Needle Crop of Sainte-Dodo *(France)*   *133*

31. Bahhh! *(France)*   *136*

32. Tales from Tartari-Barbari *(France)*   *142*

33. Peter's Adventures *(Denmark)*   *147*

34. Faithful Legs and Lazy Head *(Gypsy)*   *156*

35. The Man, the Woman, and the Fly *(Iceland)*   *161*

36. Fools' Bells Ring in Every Town *(Italy)*   *164*

37. Giufá and the Judge *(Italy)*   *173*

38. Donkey and Scholars *(Flemish)*   *175*

39. Silly Matt *(Norway)*   *180*

40. The Schilda Town Hall *(Germany)* *184*

41. The Stove and the Town Hall *(Germany)* *189*

42. The Tailor from the Sea *(Finland)* *192*

43. Aili's Quilt *(Finland)* *196*

44. Kultani, the Noodle Gossip *(Finland)* *202*

45. The Obedient Servant *(Hungary)* *207*

46. The Hero *(Hungary)* *212*

47. Luck for Fools *(Austria)* *216*

48. Tandala and Pakala *(Rumania)* *222*

49. Belmont Antics *(Switzerland)* *229*

50. Lutonya *(Russia)* *235*

51. The Tale of the Men of Prach *(Yugoslavia)* *241*

52. Smartness for Sale *(Yugoslavia)* *244*

53. The Moon in the Donkey *(Spain)* *249*

54. Not on the Lord's Day *(Portugal)* *253*

55. The Wolf in the Sack *256*

56. Juan Bobo *(Puerto Rico)* *260*

57. Noodlehead Pat *(Canada)* *263*

58. The Sombreros of the Men of Lagos *(Mexico)* *268*

59. The "Foolish People" *(U.S.A.)* *271* ✔

60. Little Head, Big Medicine *(U.S.A.)* *274* ✔

61. Sam'l Dany, Noodlehead *(U.S.A.)* *278*

62. Noodlehead Luck *(U.S.A.)* *281*

63. John in the Storeroom *(U.S.A.)* *284*

64. Kibbe's Shirt *(U.S.A.)* *287*

Notes *291*

ILLUSTRATIONS

So he let them pull out his hairs one after another until— 27

He counted the donkeys again—and again there were only nine. 65

The next morning, there was the banging and hammering as usual. 83

"Why not use the clothes?" said the hodja. "They will not need them tomorrow." 107

"If you put one pack on one shoulder and another on the other, it will weigh less." 125

"B-b-b-Bahhh!" Lamkin bleated. 139

"You, faithful legs, deserve a soft pillow." 159

The sun bird stood crowing kikeriki. 169

But after she covered his neck, his feet were once more out in the cold. 199

"Numskull! Dolt! Didn't you see the wheels sliding off!" 209

"A sister to that witch turned the wool you sold me into old turnip leaves." 227

"Here are fine jackets no one wants," one of the fellows said with a twinkle in his eye. 233

NOODLEHEAD STORIES

from around the world

PLANT A STORY—REAP A STORY

A storyteller's introduction

I have traveled all over the world telling stories and listening to stories. Whether I was in Sweden or France or Turkey or Italy or any other place, I'd tell tales about Johnny Darling of New York or Abe Lincoln of Illinois or Mike Fink from out West, and someone listening would come back with a tale to match mine. So, you see, plant a story and you reap a story.

Now, I like tales of laughter and pleasure more than I like tales of murder and fear. When people laugh, I am sure there is joy in heaven. So I usually tell tales that bring a smile to the lips and warmth to the heart. That always means a sunny tale in return, and that is why I have notebooks full and memories full and often tapes full of funny stories.

But I didn't have to go all over the world to find the tales in this book. Living in New York City, I could have gathered them right here. There isn't a land on earth that hasn't sent some of its people to Manhattan Island.

There are also, in New York City, the men and women at the United Nations Assembly, gathered from every corner of the earth to keep peace in the world. Visit their building, particularly when they come together for fun and frolic, and you will hear every tale in this book and hosts more to boot.

Noodleheads began when man began doing silly and foolish deeds, which means they began when man began. The tales of their deeds have always been a source of amusement.

What is a Noodlehead? He is a very simple person; or a silly one; or a blundering one; or one who does not use reason or learning; or one who does not learn by experience. Don't think that's where the land of Noodledom and Noodleheads stops. Sometimes even people with understanding will do a noddie deed at a particular time—for example, when one loses reason because, say, of the desire to grab too much. The result is often the silliest and most stupid behavior in the world.

Often too much pride will make a Noodlehead out of a person, as you'll see in the Tiger and the Fox.

Some scholars, as in Greece, became famous for their stupid deeds. Again, folks who like to use big, fat words they don't understand can make perfect fools of themselves. Some famous plays have been written in England about such ninnies.

Often, people who try to cheat or bully do stupid things instead, and what do they become? Noodleheads, of course.

Even a very smart person may turn into a goose cap of the silliest kind, as when a Smart Alec tries to pull a mean trick on someone kind or good. Often just losing one's temper, like the fox in the story, will make one lunkheaded.

Now, folks enjoy laughing at hoddy-doddies—so much so, that in nearly every country in the world such tales have grown up around whole towns or communities, even in our own America. In New York City the people who live in Manhattan poke fun at those living in Brooklyn. I'm sure nearly every city laughs at the deeds of some neighboring city.

Who has not heard of Gotham in England, Sainte Dodo in France, Abdara and Cumae in Greece, Chelm in Poland, Montieri in Italy, and so on through the world? Almost every country has a town that is the Kingdom of Ninnies.

Of course, the fun is good-natured and in the spirit of fun-poking.

Sometimes one individual wears his country's nit-wit crown. Endless tales are built around such a person, and in a way he becomes a hero—a folk hero. There is Nasur-ud-Din in Turkey, Giufá in Italy, Sancho Panza in Spain, and so on. Most countries have such famous personalities.

One of the very interesting facts about the stories of their deeds is their similarity in lands thousands of miles apart. Stories found in Finland and Denmark are told in Japan and Russia, Iceland or France, as you will learn in the notes. The funny story about the "Foolish People" found among the Apache Indian tribes in the United States is also found in Iceland, told in a slightly different way because of the different environment. Stories about two famous Croatian sillies, Lala and Sosa, which were told to me by two good Yugoslavian friends, are told in Texas and Maine.

This is really not surprising. People are very much alike. They all have noses, and flies get on all of them.

Scholars say these Noodlehead folk stories began in India and from there spread throughout the world as the people of India migrated. But this does not change the picture. The fact that the same stories spread everywhere proves that there is a sameness of taste, a sameness of character and situation the whole world round.

Silly sons are everywhere; there are silly daughters-in-law everywhere. There are silly people all over the world, and under certain conditions they all act the same way. Thus the same story can be true everywhere except for some slight change that is not important.

Of course, pretty nearly all the tales in this book can be found in many other books told a little differently. Anyone who is interested in them from an anthropological or social or historical point of view could have a great deal of fun comparing them. Professor Stith Thompson has written a most excellent work on the folk story that would be very valuable in such a study. In the invaluable Folk-story Index by Professors Aarne and Thompson you will find gathered the parallels of almost all the folk stories known. W. A. Clouston's book, in which he collected many Noodlehead tales from all over the world, is of great value as well.

In conclusion, I would like to say I have actually heard nearly all these stories and I have told them as I heard them. When I found them in books in slightly different versions, I did not change my own way of telling them. After all, each storyteller tells tales in his own way and no two storytellers tell a story exactly alike.

So say I, and so said Seumas MacManus one night in

my home, and so says Richard Chase, the peer among American storytellers, and so says every true story-teller.

Here are the Noodlehead stories as I tell them—and in telling them keep in mind what a great Jewish scholar said a long time ago: "There is holy truth in all stories and jests."

M.J.

1. THE HORSE-EGG

(India)

There was once a guru in India—that is, a teacher—
who had five disciples, or pupils, who followed him to
learn his wisdom. His pupils would have been fine
scholars if only they hadn't been such Noodleheads.

One day the pupils were talking while the guru
was sleeping.

"Our master is the greatest master in all India and
we are lucky to be his pupils. If only we could give
him as rich gifts as he gives us," said one.

"He walks all day long on the roads and through
the villages and we listen to his golden words. He
must be very tired sometimes," said another.

"If he had a horse to ride on, he wouldn't be tired,"
said a third.

"Let us put all our money together and buy our master a horse."

All of them agreed that this was a wonderful scheme. So they put all their money into a bag, and two of the scholars were sent to buy the guru a fine horse.

They walked along in the hot sun, and when it became too hot, they sat down in the shade of a tree.

A villager came by, a sly fellow, a bag full of green watermelons on his back. He, too, felt hot, so he sat down beside the scholars, and they began to talk. And since words from the mouth tell the thoughts in the mind, the villager soon knew these two were the kind who would go fishing for the moon in the water.

They soon told their business, which was to buy a fine horse for their guru, to save him from walking.

"Good friends, you don't have to walk farther. I am the very horse dealer for whom you are looking. But first I must tell you that you should be happy to have such a wise guru, and your guru should be very happy to have such faithful pupils. A horse is a fine animal for one who has to walk too much. I have many horses to sell. Young ones and old ones. But horses are expensive today. Why not buy a horse-egg and hatch your own horse? Thus you are sure to get a young, strong, healthy beast that will serve your master for many years."

"A horse-egg! That would be just the right thing to buy," the younger of the pupils said. "Do you have any of these eggs for sale?"

"I have. In this bag I am carrying some horse eggs to the next village to sell and I'll sell one to you." He opened his bag and showed them the green water-melons. "How much money have you?"

They told him.

"I will give you for that the largest and finest horse-egg I have. It should hatch the best colt in all the land for your master. And it is almost ready to open. All you have to do is to sit on it a short time, and the animal will come out."

The young scholars gave him the money, and he gave them the green watermelon.

Heat or no heat, they ran back, the precious horse-egg in their arms, and told their beloved guru of their great luck. The guru seemed very pleased.

"It is the first time I have ever seen a horse-egg, but years bring wisdom. I myself will sit on this egg that will give me the animal, and I want to thank you for your fine gift. Now, my good pupils, I must go to the next village quickly. You follow me slowly with the horse-egg, and tonight I will sit on it to hatch the colt."

He went off and the pupils followed, two of them carrying the watermelon. They walked in front of the others. Thus they marched through the roads and fields and came to a little hillock. There the two carrying the precious load stumbled over a tree stump. The watermelon fell out of their hands, rolled down a little way, then hit a tree and—broke in two. A hare, hidden in the brush, was frightened and leaped out and away.

There were cries and confusion when the melon fell and broke, and there were greater cries when they saw the hare leap away. They thought it was a young horse that had come out of the watermelon.

"There goes the young horse of our master!" "What will we tell him?" "Did you see him run?" "He was such a swift steed." "He flew as swift as an arrow!" "He was fit for a king!" "There is none like him in all India!"

Thus they shouted and wailed and kept on shouting and wailing until they reached the village where the guru was waiting.

"Alas, Master," they cried together, "a great misfortune has happened. We dropped the horse-egg while we were on our way, and it broke, and out ran the young colt and disappeared before our very eyes!" "It ran swifter than the wind!" "The king has not such a swift horse!" "Truly it was a horse for the gods!" "Oh, what a great misfortune!" "We wept all the way."

But the guru was a wise teacher. "My good scholars," he said, "do not weep. It is not so great a misfortune as you think. Since the young horse was swifter
than the wind, it was not a horse for me. I am an old
man and a quiet one and a scholar. I do not like to go
fast, even on a horse. Such an animal is for a young
warrior. If I had gotten on that horse it would have
carried me away from you, my good scholars, and that
would have made me very unhappy. Rejoice, my pupils, and be grateful that the horse's egg broke where
it did and that the young colt ran off, swift as the
wind. Thus you saved me from breaking my neck and
have kept me healthy among you. So you see that misfortune in this case was good."

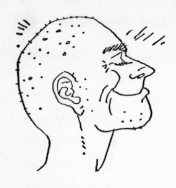

2. DON'T MARRY TWO WIVES

(India)

In Balochi, in India, there lived a man who was so silly he married two wives. And, I want to tell you, those two wives made that Noodlehead dance to every tune they played.

One day the three were sitting in their cool chamber, for the day was hot. The husband was sitting before one of his two wives, and she was combing his *choti*—that is, his hair. She was talking like a running river. Suddenly she saw a white *choti* among the black of her husband's head. She took it tight between her thumb and forefinger and pulled it out.

"Ouch!" the husband cried.

"What did you do to our good husband?" the second wife asked.

"I pulled a white hair from his head."

"How dare you do that!" cried the second. "White hair in a man's head is a sign of wisdom. You should never have pulled that hair out. Give me that white hair from our husband's head. I will treasure it like a jewel."

"I will not give it to you, it's mine," cried the first.

"I want that hair!" screamed the second. "You have no right to have a hair and I none."

So they screamed back and forth, one wanting the hair and the other refusing it.

The husband was thinking all this time of how to bring peace between his two wives and peace to his ears. In the end he said:

"Wives, good wives, don't quarrel. You," speaking to the first, "keep the white hair. And you, dear wife," speaking to the second, "pull out one of my black hairs. Then you will each have a hair."

The second wife pulled out a black hair at once, whereupon the first began to scream: "She has a black hair and I have a white one. That is not fair. A black hair is worth more than a white hair." She kept on screaming this over and over while the silly husband was wondering how he could stop the noise. Then a smile came to his face and he said:

"Dear wife, don't cry. Come, you pull a black hair out of my head. Then you will have a black hair, too. That will make you happy."

The woman pulled out a black hair at once, making a face at the second wife.

Then the second wife screamed, "She has a black hair and a white hair. She has two hairs and I have only one." She kept it up without end. The silly husband looked and thought, and again a smile came to his face, for he had the answer.

"Wife," said he cheerfully, "don't scream and cry. You can have two hairs, too. Pull out another black hair from my head and you will have two."

This the woman did. But at once the first wife began screaming and wailing.

"You love her more than you do me. You let her have two black hairs and I have only one. You are a fine husband!"

She kept on and on until the husband said:

"Dear wife, don't cry, now you pull a black hair out of my head, so you will have two black hairs, too."

She did that at once, and then the second wife began to wail and cry once more.

"She has three hairs and I have only two; you love her more than you love me. She has three hairs, and I have only two!" The husband listened till his ears ached, and then he said:

So he let them pull out his hairs one after another until—
there was not a hair left on his head!

"Dearest wife, you pull out another black hair, and then you will have three."

No sooner had the second pulled out the third black hair than the first screamed she had only two black hairs, and when the husband let her pull out another black hair, the second screamed that she had only three hairs and the first had four.

There was no peace. For it did not matter how many black hairs were pulled out of that Noodlehead, the two wives never had an equal number of hairs. The first one, who had pulled out the first white hair, always had one more, and the second always had one less.

The silly fellow never thought of that, so he let them pull out his black hairs one after another, until— there was not a hair left on his head! He was all bald, and his head was full of red pimples from the hair-pulling. But there was a happy smile on his face, for now the chamber was silent. Neither of the wives said a word.

"How quiet and peaceful we three are," said the husband. "Now we are all happy."

3. THE NOODLEHEAD TIGER

(India)

In Baluchistan, in far India, there lived a fierce tiger in the deep green jungle. He was sleek and slithery, with long stripes and cruel long teeth. Day and night he stalked through the thick jungle tearing animals to pieces, whether he needed food or not.

Now, you know those who are cruel and greedy often turn into Noodleheads because they can't think. And that tiger had become stupid and insolent with his greediness and cruelty.

All the animals in the jungle were afraid of him; no one was safe. It was impossible to live in the jungle any more, and so the animals got together to hold a council. Everybody came, from the hare to the elephant, and there was much talk—and every word was full of fear. In the end they decided the only way left was to tell the mad tiger that each day one animal would come to him to be eaten—if he would let the others live in peace. It wasn't the best plan in the world, but it was the best they could think of.

They told this to the wild tiger. He gnashed his teeth, then he sneered:

"That will do until I change my mind."

From then on, each day an animal went meekly to be devoured by the tiger—until the fox's turn came.

This was a very foxy fox. He was so foxy that even fear did not frighten him. He was walking slowly through the woods, thinking.

"I don't want to be eaten," he thought to himself, "and there must be some way out. That tiger is so greedy and stupid that he is blind in his head and cannot think. I am sure he is a Noodlehead and that it will be easy to trick him." Then an idea came to him and with a big smile on his face he walked more and more slowly. Finally he came to the tiger's cave. When the tiger saw the fox he roared:

"Why are you so late? What kept you so long?"

"Oh, King Tiger, forgive me! I couldn't come more quickly to be eaten by your royal teeth. But if I hadn't come late, you wouldn't have any breakfast at all."

"What do you mean," bellowed the tiger, "I

wouldn't have any breakfast at all? Weren't you to come here to be eaten?"

"Indeed, indeed I was, King Tiger, and that is why it took me so long. I had to keep out of sight of a terrible new tiger who has come into our jungle and who wanted to eat me for breakfast. I had to sneak through the jungle, around and around, to escape him so you could make a nice breakfast of me. That tiger is a fierce tiger with stripes even bigger than yours."

"Where is that new tiger?" roared the tiger. "I'll show him what I can do to him. Lead me to where he is right now. I can eat you later."

Quickly the fox ran through the jungle, zigzagging over stumps and clumps in all directions while the tiger followed him closely, gnashing his teeth and swishing his tail.

Suddenly the fox stopped and turned to the tiger.

"Sh . . . sh . . ." he whispered. "We are getting close to him. Soon you'll see him . . . where he is hiding. When you see him, leap on him and tear him to pieces."

The fox slithered along slowly, the tiger behind him. They came to a clearing where there was a deep, dark well.

"He is down there," whispered the fox.

The tiger snarled, pulled back his lips, showing his long teeth, and his tail snapped like a whip. He looked down the well and there he saw a tiger gnashing his teeth and moving his thick lips fiercely up and down.

With a roar, the tiger leaped into the well at the face that showed in the water. . . . And that was the end of the Noodlehead tiger.

The foxy fox went off happily through the jungle. Soon he met an antelope.

"Why are you here?" cried the antelope. "You were to be eaten by the tiger. Do you want to bring misery back to all the animals of the jungle again?"

"There'll be no misery from now on," the fox replied. "Sister Antelope, when an animal becomes greedy and fierce, it loses understanding and becomes a Noodlehead. That tiger was so greedy and cruel that there was no room for good sense in his head. When he saw his own face in the well he thought it was another tiger and jumped in to eat him. Now he is at the bottom of the well and there is no tiger."

4. THERE ARE SUCH PEOPLE

(India)

Once there lived a couple, a husband and a wife. What kind of people were they? You'll soon find out.

They went to sleep one night and a strong wind came up—a wind that shook the trees and houses. The wind blew their door open.

"Husband," said the wife, "close the door, for the wind will blow things on our heads."

"You close it. I am tired; I worked all day in the field."

"And I worked all day in the house. You close it."

"My work was harder than yours, wife. You close the door."

"My work was without end. You are stronger, husband. You close the door."

"I will not," the silly fellow said. "You work more with your mouth than with your hands."

"I will not," the silly wife said. "This is a man's work."

So they kept on with this Noodlehead argument for a long time, just shouting at each other. They were so deep in their silly argument they never saw a man, a thief, standing at the door listening to them.

The game kept on, the two blabbering, the wind whistling, and the thief listening, with neither the husband nor the wife getting up from the bed to shut the door. In the end the husband said:

"I'll tell you what. I am tired of talking and I won't talk any more. It's time you were quiet, too. Let the one who speaks first close the door."

The wife agreed, and at last there was silence in the room. Each lay in the bed, eyes open, lips shut, waiting for the other to speak.

The thief standing at the door watched them for a while. "Here's a pair of fools for you," he said to himself. "I will reap the benefit of their folly."

He walked in boldly and stood in the middle of the room.

Neither the silly wife nor the silly husband said a word.

"Ha! There's a pair of Noodleheads! I can do my work," the thief said aloud.

He took all the things he wanted—clothes, jewels, pots—and made a bundle of them.

Neither the husband nor wife said a word.

The thief took the bundle outside.

Still not a word was said.

"Never have I seen such numskulls in my life," the thief mumbled to himself. "I must have a little more fun out of this."

He went to the griddle on the fireplace and smeared his hands full of soot. Then he smeared the soot all over the man's face, then over the woman's face.

Neither uttered a sound.

The thief walked out, saying to himself, "These are the worst fools in all the world."

The man and the wife lay in bed the whole night long, and the wind blew wildly through the open door in their half-empty house.

But neither spoke a word.

The sky reddened and the birds were singing and the sun came up over the village. It was full daylight. Both sat up and looked at each other, lips shut tight. The man saw the woman's black face; the woman saw the man's black face. She cried out:

"Husband, your face is all black."

"You spoke first," the husband said. "Now you shut the door."

There are such people in the world.

5. DO YOU KNOW?

(Greece)

In the days when the Greeks built beautiful temples of white marble, the boys and girls who lived in that country in the bright cities and swam along the gleaming shores were no different from boys and girls of today. They played the same kinds of games, they did the same kind of work, and they often listened to the same kinds of stories. They surely must have had funny "Do You Know?" guessing games.

Now, in those days there was one group of people in Greece at whom everybody, young and old, laughed. These were certain scholars and teachers and philosophers who always kept their noses in books and always held endless discussions and arguments about windy nothings in words no one could understand. There were many of these scholars and teachers and philosophers, and they thought they were better than everybody else, though they were really only very silly. The funniest stories you can imagine were told about them by everyone. Whenever young folks got together in the cities near the white marble temples or forums or at the seashore, where gilded and green painted chariots and donkeys laden with baskets of green figs and white garlic came by, one would begin:

"Do you know about the silly philosopher who met another silly philosopher?"

"What happened?"

"Well, the first one said to the second one, 'Master, I saw you in a dream three days ago and spoke to you.'

"Answered the second, 'By the gods, Master, you couldn't!'

" 'Why not?' asked the first.

" 'Because three days ago I was away on my vacation.' "

And then another boy or girl in a white tunic and sandals or bare feet might say:

"Do you know about the master who wanted to know what he looked like when he was asleep?"

"No."

"What do you think he did?"

"I don't know."

"Why, the silly stood before the mirror and . . . and closed his eyes."

And of course there would be laughter.

Then another might say: "Do you know what happened to one of those silly philosophers when he was walking in the garden one afternoon?"

"No."

"He saw a flock of birds on a tree and wanted some of them. Guess how he tried to catch them."

"With snares?"

"Oh, no. He spread his cloak under the tree and shook the tree for the birds to fall down."

They could tell these "Do You Know?" stories for hours, just as you and I can.

6. THE DONKEY OF ABDERA

(Greece)

The ancient Greeks said the silly people of their country came mainly from Abdera, from Sidonia, from Cumae, and from Boeotia.

Now, the white town of Abdera was divided into two parts, the East and the West.

Those who lived in the eastern part of the town made sport of those who lived in the western part of the town, and those who lived in the western part of the town made sport of those who lived in the eastern part.

Abdera, like other cities, had a fine gymnasium where men and boys came for exercise and gossip.

One glowing day an ass that belonged to an olive merchant wandered away, as donkeys often do, and came to the gymnasium. The donkey liked the white marble columns and the big building so he went inside.

It was then the hot noon hour, when people were resting. In the high chamber there were tunics lying around, and in the corner stood a green jar full of olive oil that was used by the athletes.

The donkey, nosy like all donkeys, sniffed at everything, hoping to find some food. Finally he came to the green jar filled with olive oil. Nosing it all over with his thick lips and big teeth in a clumsy way, he pushed it a little too hard and—crck! the green jar went over. The oil poured out on the ground and the pieces of the jar went in every direction on the white marble floor.

The gymnasium attendants, who were eating their noon meal of bread, cheese, and olives, rushed in at the noise and saw the donkey splattering in the oil on the floor and the pieces of the broken jar.

"Look what that beast has done! He must be punished for that! Hang the culprit!" they all cried.

"No," said the oldest. "Such a great crime must be judged by all the citizens of Abdera. We will call a meeting at the Forum to decide the punishment."

The meeting was called in the Forum and all the citizens came. There were fiery speeches condemning the donkey's crime, and in the end it was decided to flog the donkey publicly and . . . something else! To avoid such a crime again, all the asses of Abdera were to be brought to watch the punishment and so learn that it did not pay to commit crimes.

The flap-eared evildoer was brought to the public marketplace and everybody was there. Citizens who had donkeys brought them along. Those with the donkeys stood in the front row, holding the faces of their donkeys toward the square. In the center stood the long-eared criminal, and next to him, the proper officer. Then the donkey was punished, and the men of Abdera cried:

"Watch, you donkeys, and learn what happens to a donkey who turns over oil jars in the gymnasium. May the punishment of this wicked one teach you asses wisdom."

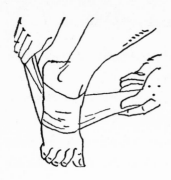

7. BAREFOOT IN BED

(Greece)

One night a silly scholar of Abdera was visiting another scholar who was just as silly as he was. The two ate more than was good for them. After the feast the first scholar walked home and went to sleep. But his sleep was very restless and full of dreams, as often happens when you eat too much. He had all kinds of nightmares. The last one, just at dawn, made him get up with a great cry and in pain. He dreamed he was walking in the city and accidentally stepped on a long nail that nearly went through his foot. It hurt and he was frightened, and then he awoke.

"I must tie the wound on my foot," he cried. "It hurts and I must not get any dirt in it."

He tied it up carefully with a few bandages, then he had his breakfast, and then he went limping to the gymnasium, where men went to exercise and to gossip. There he met other sillies—Noodleheads, like himself.

"What happened to you, Master?" they all cried when they saw him limping in. "What happened to you?"

The limping scholar then told how he had dreamed his foot had been terribly hurt with a long, rusty nail.

"The pain was awful," he said. "That nail nearly went through my foot. I could see the other end of it sticking out."

Every one of his friends sympathized with him, and one white-haired teacher said:

"Master, I will tell you how to avoid such accidents, for they can be tragic. In fact, I have known a man to die from having a nail go through his foot. Here is a way to avoid such terrible mishaps: The next time you go to bed, don't go barefoot—just wear your sandals."

All the scholars thought this was excellent advice, and the one with the "wound" in his foot promised that in the future he would always go to bed with his sandals on.

8. THE FOX IN THE HOLE

(Jewish)

In the olden, golden days of the Jews, when they lived in their own kingdom in Israel (even as they do to-day), there dwelt a fox outside the city of Jerusalem amid the vineyards and the fields. He was a very stupid fox; nay, he was a Noodlehead. Why was he a Noodlehead? Because no matter how much he had of anything, he always wanted more, and that made him so blind that he always acted stupidly.

Not far from where the fox lived was the home of a rich merchant, a house surrounded by a rich garden in which grew the finest fruits around Jerusalem. The silly fox always had his eyes on that garden, but, no matter how he tried, he could not get into it. Its walls were strong and tight, except for one small hole—a hole too small for the fat fox to slide through.

All summer the fox watched the fruit through the hole, and when the pears and apples and grapes began to ripen, the fox's tongue hung down with covetous desire. For he was too stupid to know that greediness is the mother of ruin.

Each day the pears looked rosier and the grapes shone brighter and the fox was jumping out of his skin to get at the fruit.

Again and again he stood before the hole in the wall, trying to see if he couldn't get through, but only his head could enter. His body was too fat and just couldn't make any headway. One day, as he stood before that hole in the wall, he had an idea.

"If I only could make my body as thin as my head, I could get into the garden and at those grapes. From to-day on I will not eat until my body is as thin as my head, and then I'll get into the garden. I'll starve myself, and then I'll have the finest feast of my life."

For three days the fox took no food, and at the end his body was as thin as his head.

He went to the hole and slid into the garden easily and had the finest feast of his life. Lush pears and tender grapes and juicy apples. He ate and he ate to make up for all his months of waiting and for the three days he had starved himself.

On the third day in the garden, he heard the servants of the merchant say they would come in four days to harvest the crop, and the fox decided it was time to leave. He went to the hole through which he had come and . . . found that only his head could get through. Again and again he tried, but he never got farther than his neck.

"If the servants find me here, they will kill me. I must get out," the fox said. "But how?"

The next morning came.

"In three days the servants will be here, and if I don't get out, it will be the end of me. I must get out as I came in. And I came in by starving myself for three days.

"It is a terrible thing to starve one's self. It was not so bad when I did it before, because I knew I was coming in to a great feast. But now I will go out and there will be no feast waiting. What makes it even worse is that now I will starve myself in the midst of plenty. Woe is me! But what can I do? I don't want to die."

So the silly fox again starved himself for three days, and at the end of that time his body was as thin as his head and he wiggled out of the garden.

9. THE GOLDEN SHOES

(Jewish)

The city of Chelm, in Poland, is just as famous as the city of Gotham in England. It is as famous as any city in the world where men believed that billy goats had one short beard in front and a long beard in back that other men call tails. To prove it, I'll tell you how the men of Chelm solved one of the great problems in their community.

The citizens of Chelm had heard that every great city in the land had a chief sage—that is, a man who was a greater teacher of the Law than any other great teacher of the Law, a man who was wiser than any other man, one who commanded respect not only in his own town but in every town in Poland. Chelm was a famous city and it, too, deserved the honor of having a chief sage.

A town meeting was held and everyone made three long speeches. In the end, the citizens chose their chief sage. They were proud and happy, but their pride and joy did not last long.

They noted that when their chief sage walked slowly through the town, stroking his long beard, no one even noticed him. Other men also walked slowly and stroked their beards. The chief sage looked just like any other man—like a shoemaker or a tailor. That would never do! A chief sage must look like a chief sage. Different!

A town meeting was called to consider this problem. After long arguments it was decided to buy the chief sage a pair of golden shoes. Then he would look different, and all the world would notice him. Seeing him, people would say:

"There goes the chief sage of Chelm with his golden shoes."

They bought the golden shoes, and the chief sage put them on and walked proudly through the streets. But alas! The streets of Chelm were just mud. It was spring, and the rains had made the mud so soft that shoes sank into it ankle deep. The golden shoes were all covered with mud, and no one noticed the chief sage.

This made him angry, and he went straight to the Council of Common Sages.

"No one notices me, and if something isn't done about it, I resign."

"Your complaint is just, and we don't blame you for your righteous anger. If we were in your place, we would do the same." That's what the ordinary sages said in one voice. "But have patience, we will think of something. The dignity of our chief sage must be upheld and protected."

They discussed the matter and then decided to order a pair of ordinary shoes for the chief sage to wear over his golden shoes—and so protect them from the mud.

The shoes were made, and the chief sage put them on over the golden shoes. But now there was new trouble. The ordinary shoes hid the golden shoes, and again no one noticed the chief sage. This made him angrier than ever, and he rushed to the Council of Common Sages and cried:

"Worthy sages of Chelm, who chose me as your chief sage, what's the use of being your chief sage? No one shows me proper respect. I resign."

"Don't do this, great sage. Don't do this, respected one. We will find a remedy. Trust us."

They delved into the problem and then decided they had an answer. The shoemaker was ordered to make a new pair of shoes over the golden shoes, and these should have holes on the sides through which the golden shoes would shine. Thus the folks of Chelm and from other towns would recognize the chief sage at once and pay him proper respect.

So it was done, and the chief sage put on the new shoes. But they didn't help. The mud got into the holes of the new shoes, no one saw the golden shoes, and no one looked at the chief sage. He was deeply mortified and stormed into the Council of Common Sages.

"This is the end. I am ashamed to show my face in the streets. Not a person even looks at me. What's the use of being the chief sage? No one shows me proper respect. I resign!"

"Learned master," they said again, "we will find a remedy."

They held a feverish discussion, and this time it was decided to fill the holes of the overshoes with straw so that the mud could not get in. The straw protected the golden shoes against the mud, but . . . it also hid the golden shoes from sight. And once again the chief sage walked around unnoticed.

The good man came to the Council with tears in his eyes and anger in his voice.

"Lord on high!" he cried. "Will there be no end to my mortification? It's no use. Your chief sage is nothing but a common man and he is finished. This time, for good."

"No, no, a thousand times no!" the common sages cried. "Holy teacher, give us one more chance."

"That I will. But remember, this is your very last chance."

Once again the ordinary sages went into a profound discussion. The situation was argued from both the earthly and the heavenly sides. There were passionate speeches until the earth shook and the stars blinked. Then an inspiration came over one of the lesser sages. The others listened and then they sang and danced with joy. Then they called the chief sage.

"Blessed be the Holy One! We have found the right answer to our prayers, and the solution to our perplexing problem. From this day on, you will be honored and recognized in a manner that is due your exalted position, great Chief Sage of Chelm. Here is our answer.

"From now on, you will wear the golden shoes on your hands instead of on your feet. No mud will darken their splendor; all the world will recognize you as the great Chief Sage of Chelm!"

So it was done, and from then on everyone knew when the great Chief Sage of Chelm walked through the streets of the city with the golden shoes on his hands.

10. THE GREAT TRAVELER
OF CHELM

(Jewish)

There lived in Chelm a man who loved traveling more than anything in the world. He was always dreaming of going to different cities. When men spoke of far places, he would listen not only with his ears but with his mouth and eyes as well. His name was Benjamin, and he truly would have given half his years to visit other lands.

One time, a Chelm merchant visited Warsaw. Since no one in Chelm ever went out of the town, this was a great event. When the merchant returned, Chelm hummed with the tales of his adventures. All day long and far into the night everyone listened to him telling about the wonders of Warsaw.

"There were millions of people in Warsaw. There was no mud in the streets. The houses were high as heaven. Truly, it was a Garden of Eden on earth."

No one listened more greedily to these tales than Benjamin, and in his heart there sprang up a fierce desire to see Warsaw. Never had he been away from Chelm, but now he was going out on this great adventure.

He did not say a word about this to his wife until the day before he was ready. Then he said:

"Esther, my wife," said he, "I am going to travel to Warsaw."

"Just like that? Why are you going to Warsaw? What has come over you, Benjamin, my husband? Are you in your right mind?"

"Of course, I am in my right mind, Esther, my good wife, and I am going to Warsaw. All my life I have wanted to travel, and now I will do it."

"How will you travel? You have no money to pay for a ride."

"I will walk."

"You will wear out your best shoes."

"I will walk barefoot and carry the shoes in my hands."

"You will hurt your feet."

"Our good God will watch over me."

Benjamin had made up his mind to go to Warsaw, and he was firm as a mountain.

The next morning, early, he rose, put bread and cheese in a kerchief, and set out.

He walked and he walked and he was very happy. He felt like singing and dancing. He was traveling to see new sights, new cities, the great city of Warsaw!

Noon came and he was hungry, so he sat down under a tree, took out his cheese and bread, and began eating. When he was through, he wanted to have a little sleep. "That will refresh me and toward evening I should be in the great city of Warsaw. But I must remember the road. All the roads look so much alike. Whichever way I look, whether it's from Chelm, from where I came, or toward Warsaw, where I am going, God be willing, it is the same kind of road. I must be careful not to get lost. Well, that's easy. I'll set my shoes [remember, Benjamin carried his shoes in his hands and walked barefoot] with the toes pointing toward Warsaw. Then I'll be sure to go in the right direction." Pleased with his wisdom, he lay down and soon fell asleep. While he was dreaming of the wonderful city he would soon see, a peasant passed by in a cart and saw the shoes on the ground.

"I need a pair of shoes, and I am sure this man sleeping left them here for me," he thought.

He picked up the shoes but, after looking at them, threw them back on the ground.

"Those shoes have more holes than a sieve. They aren't worth taking," he said, and rode off.

Accidentally he had thrown them down with the toes pointing in the direction of Chelm instead of toward Warsaw, as Benjamin had left them.

Soon Benjamin awoke refreshed and full of the joy of adventure.

"There are the shoes pointing in the direction in which I am to go," he cried gaily.

He picked up the shoes and began walking the way they pointed . . . in the direction of Chelm!

Soon he saw a city and entered with great excitement. But his excitement changed to surprise, and with each step his surprise became greater and greater.

"As I live and breathe, Warsaw looks almost the same as Chelm," he said to himself. "And Moses the leather merchant said it looked so much different. I am afraid Moses was not telling the truth."

He looked at the people in the street.

"As I believe in a true God! If the people here in Warsaw do not look exactly like the people in my home town! The same faces, the same clothes, the same beards!"

He came to the House of God. The *shamas*—that is, the beadle—standing outside, asked him to come in.

"There is no end to wonders in this world. The beadle in Warsaw looks exactly like the beadle in Chelm—as like as one egg to another. And the people in the Holy House of Warsaw look like the people in the Holy House of Chelm. It is a very unusual coincidence."

He left the Holy House and walked along the street and there . . . everyone looked exactly the same as the people in Chelm.

"If I didn't know I was in Warsaw, I'd swear by the Almighty I was in Chelm," he mumbled to himself.

He couldn't believe his eyes. Now he was on a street that looked exactly like his own street in Chelm, and there a child was playing who looked like his own son at home. Truly, that was a miracle!

Then he thought he was dreaming, for at the door of a house that looked exactly like his own house stood a woman who, if he did not know he was in Warsaw, he would have sworn was his own wife. Oh, yes, she had a twin sister, but even she couldn't look so much like his wife!

"Come in the house and have your meal, Benjamin. Don't stand in the middle of the street looking as if your eyes would jump out of your head."

"Can this be possible?" muttered Benjamin. "The voice—everything—it's just like Esther at home. And she called me by my name! Truly, I never read of such a marvel in the holy writings. Two cities, a day's distance apart, and streets, houses, and . . . people exactly alike."

He went into the house.

"Why, even the furniture is exactly as in my house in Chelm. And there is the smell of burned meat, just as in my home in Chelm!"

Benjamin was bewildered.

"This woman here in Warsaw looks like my wife in Chelm. But I am in Warsaw! There are happenings in the world beyond man's understanding. But what I really would like to know is whether there is someone exactly like me, with my name, living here in Warsaw. And where is he? Maybe he went to Chelm and he is in my house! Maybe the best thing is for me to wait here and let him make this clear to me."

"Stop mumbling to yourself and sit down to eat," his wife said.

Benjamin sat down without saying another word.

The men of Chelm were famous for their patience, and when Benjamin decided to wait, he meant to wait. And so he waited. And I wouldn't be surprised if he is still waiting there. It would be just like a man of Chelm to do that!

11. FIGS FOR GOLD, FIGS FOR FOLLY

(Jewish)

This is a tale of a wise man and a Noodlehead that is told in the ancient books of the Jews.

The wise one, an old man, was digging in his garden near Tiberias in Galilee, in Israel, planting fig trees. The Emperor Hadrian, who was then ruling over Israel, passed by and stopped and looked on in wonder.

"Old man," said he, "if you had labored in your youth, you would eat good fruit in your old age without such hard labor. Surely you cannot hope to eat the fruit from the trees you are planting now."

"Noble Emperor," the old Israelite answered, "I loved work in my youth, and I still find joy in working in my old age. If it pleases the Lord, I may eat the fruit of the trees I am planting. I am in the Lord's hands."

"How old are you, old man?" the Emperor asked.

"I am one hundred years old."

"Old man," the Emperor said with a smile, "if you live to eat the figs you are planting now, bring some to me, so I may eat them, too, for I like figs." And then the Emperor went his way.

The trees flourished, the old man lived and watched them blossom, and soon they brought forth excellent fruit. As soon as they were ripe, the old man gathered a basketful of the finest figs, put the basket on his back, and marched to the palace.

The Emperor was looking out of his window and saw the old man, bent under the weight on his shoulders, stop before the palace gate. He told the guard to bring him in.

"Why do you come to my palace, old man?"

"May it please Your Majesty, do you remember once, years ago, seeing an old man planting fig trees? You said if he lived to eat the fruit he planted, he was to bring you some. I am that old man, and here is some of the fruit I planted. I have eaten of them and now bring some to you. May it please you to accept them as a gift from me and from Our God, who let me live long enough to bring them to you."

The Emperor was pleased to see the old man. He emptied the basket of figs and filled it with gold.

"Take this," he said, "as a sign of my pleasure."

When the old man was gone, one of the courtiers asked:

"Your Majesty, why did you so honor that old Jew?"

"Why should I not honor him whom God has honored?" After that, the courtiers had nothing to say.

The old man returned to his home and showed all his neighbors and friends what a marvelous present the Emperor had given him.

"All of this for the basket of figs you brought to him!" they exclaimed.

"He likes figs," the old man answered.

Among the neighbors there was a very foolish and a very covetous woman. Without thinking, she ran to her home and cried to her husband:

"Thou son of a wretch, why tarriest thou? The Emperor likes ripe figs and gives baskets of gold for a basket of figs. Take a sackful to him, and we will become rich as our neighbor."

The husband, who was just as silly as his wife, gathered a sackful of ripe figs and carried them to the palace gate. The captain of the guard asked him what he wanted, and he said he had brought a bag of ripe figs to the Emperor and expected a big reward for it.

The captain knew what had happened and decided he would deal with this fool properly.

"You'll get your reward for coveting that which you

do not deserve," he said. "Let you remain seated at the gate and let all who pass throw your ripe figs at you. When your bag is empty, you may go home and remember not to have such big eyes for what your neighbor has."

The order was carried out, and when the bag was empty, the man went home.

His silly wife was sitting in the house figuring out how she would spend the gold her husband would bring home. When the foolish fellow came in, she cried:

"Where is the money? Your bag is empty! Is it in your pockets? What luck, husband?"

"Luck I had, base and wretched woman," the husband said. "But different from what you expected. Yet it was great and good luck just the same.

"My great luck was that I brought figs and not peaches. For, had I brought peaches instead of figs and had the peaches been thrown at my head instead of the figs, I would have been stoned to death.

"And my good luck was that the figs were ripe. If they had been green and hard, everything in my head would be at the palace gate instead of where they belong."

A fool does not see a tree as a wise man sees it.

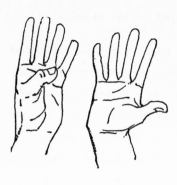

12. DONKEYS ALL

(Syria)

They tell this tale in Syria. Once there was a simpleton who bought ten donkeys to lend out for hire. But the wealth of his earthly possessions was much, much greater than his wealth of understanding.

The first day he hired out his donkeys to a woodgatherer, and at night he came to collect the beasts and get his pay. The woodgatherer returned the donkeys and gave him the money, and the man went on his way to his tent, well pleased with his day's business.

On the road it occurred to him to count the donkeys, and when he did, he found there were only nine, for he did not count the one on which he was sitting.

"That woodgatherer was a cheat and stole one of my animals," he thought.

He got off the donkey, much wrought up, and counted all over again and found that there were ten!

"That woodgatherer is not a cheat and he did not steal any of my animals," he thought.

He rode on, and as he did it occurred to him to count the animals once again. He did and . . . there were only nine, for he did not have the understanding to count the one on which he was sitting.

"That woodgatherer is the son of a thieving jackal. He took one of my donkeys."

He jumped off the donkey on which he was sitting and counted the animals all over again, and again there were . . . ten!

"The gods be thanked. I accused the man wrongfully. All the animals are here."

So he got on his donkey and rode on. But he had no peace. He could not understand why there should be a different number of donkeys each time he counted them.

"I had best count my beasts once more," he said, a deep frown on his face.

So he counted the donkeys again, and . . . there were nine.

"This is strange," he cried, leaping out of his saddle. And he counted them on the ground and . . . there were ten!

"Verily," he cried, "Satan and his brood must be

He counted the donkeys again—and again there were only nine.

around me. Whenever I mount my donkey I lose one. When I get off, the beast comes back. I think I'd better stay off altogether, because next time I mount my donkey, I may lose one for certain."

So he walked the long distance to his home on foot.

13. THE COW AND THE THREAD

(Arabia)

An Arab and his wife rose early in the morning and went out to do their daily work. In passing they looked at their house.

"Wife," said the man, "our house is all broken down. Before long we will not have a roof over our heads. It is ready to fall to pieces."

"What you say is true, indeed, good husband," she replied, "but worry belongs to the Evil One. Do not distress yourself over such a little matter. It is true we have no money to repair our house, but we have a cow worth thirty dirhems. That is what you will get at the market for her. Why not take her to the market and sell her?

"Besides that, I have a good amount of thread. I will sell it today, and between your sale and mine, I am sure we will have enough money to repair our home."

The man thought this a fine idea. He took the cow to the market and gave her to a dealer who sets the price on cattle and sells them.

The dealer showed her at once to people who stood around, ready to buy. He praised the cow's fine points and spoke so enthusiastically about the animal you would have believed she was the finest cow in all of Arabia, if not in the world.

The owner of the cow, who was a very foolish fellow, heard the praise of his cow with great surprise. He had never known he had such a fine animal.

"Allah be praised for having blessed me with such a wonderful cow," he said. "It is a lucky man who possesses her. I certainly should buy such a fine creature. I am sure my wife would be very pleased with her."

He turned to the man who was singing the praises of the cow and trying to sell her.

"Good man," said he, "what price will the cow go for?"

"I believe fifteen dirhems or more."

"By the head of the Prophet, had I known my cow possessed all these wonderful qualities, I would never have brought her to market. I shouldn't lose such a fine animal."

Now, it happened that he had with him just fifteen dirhems.

"I'll not let a chance to buy this fine animal for such a small sum pass by," he said. "Here, take the fifteen dirhems and the cow will be mine."

He took hold of the cow and went off while the dealer looked after him with open mouth, too surprised to speak.

"Never in all my years have I seen such a lame-brained fool," he said to nobody in particular.

The man ran home with his cow, overjoyed with his good luck.

"Wife, wife," he shouted when he got to the door of his old house. "Wife! I have had an hour of good fortune."

No reply. She was still in the market. He waited most impatiently. As soon as he saw her from afar, he began:

"Wife, I have done a wonderful deed. Fortune has smiled at both of us. Truly, I was favored by the sky. As the proverb says, the lamb came to the door. If . . ."

"Wait, husband, wait," she broke in. "Perhaps I, too, was favored by God. Hear my story first and then tell *me* who was the favored one."

"Who can please a woman?" the man grumbled. But she never heard him, she was so busy talking.

"When I came to the market, I found at once one who wanted to buy thread. I showed him mine. He liked it and we spoke of the price and he agreed to pay me for it by the weight. I told him how much it weighed but he did not trust me, saying he wanted to weigh it himself. He put it on the scales and I saw that it was much short of the weight I had mentioned and he refused to buy it. But I did not want to lose my chance to sell it, so I asked him to weigh it again. When his eyes were off the scale for an instant, I stripped myself of my silver bracelet and slipped it on the scales, under the thread, so he would not see it. The scale now was much heavier and I got for the thread the price I asked. That silly merchant never knew my silver bracelet made it so heavy. Now, what do you think of your wife? Am I not clever?"

"Wife, you wear a crown of wisdom. Truly, we are equal in all ways. You will agree when you hear my tale," and he related how cheaply he had gotten the most wonderful cow in Arabia.

When he was through, she said:

"Oh, husband, we are among the blessed. With your wisdom and mine, not only will our house be repaired easily, but we will overcome all other difficulties of life!"

14. CEYLON SILLIES

(Ceylon)

THE BEES IN THE WELL

The people of the village of Tumpane, in the middle of the great island of Ceylon, and the villagers of Rayigam Korle, in the southern part, are famous for their silly deeds and foolish ways.

There was a man in Tumpane who had the finest well in the village. He was very proud of it and many envied him.

Now, a swarm of wild bees had built their nest in a tree above the well, gathering the honey from the beautiful flowers that grew everywhere.

One day the man who owned the well came to get some water. He saw the picture of the bees' nest in the water of his well, and the bees swarming all around it.

"Help!" he cried. "Neighbors! My well is full of bees! They've built a nest in it. Help!"

The other villagers heard his cries, and a council was held as to what should be done.

Many spoke, and then it was decided the best thing to do was to dig up the well and put it in another place where the bees would not find it!

So everyone set to work with spades and shovels, digging all around to lift the well out of the ground. But with all the digging they could not move that well. After a time, they were tired.

"Let us leave this well to the bees," said these stupid villagers, "and we'll dig another deep one in the woods where the bees will not find it."

And so it was done!

THE MOON ON THE GROUND

In Rayigam Korle in Ceylon the villagers had planted their crops, and they were growing green to gladden men's hearts. Every day the sun, way up in the sky, drew the green blades higher and higher, and there was great rejoicing.

One night the villagers were having a feast outside

their homes. A large, yellow moon hung in the sky. When all the villagers had their fill of food and drink, they lay down on the grass.

Suddenly one of the men leaped up with a great shout.

"Look at that moon! It is coming lower and lower and will burn our fine crops," he cried.

"Let us get water to stop the fire," another shouted. Cried the others:

"It's too far to carry." "Our fine crops will be burned." "All our work will be wasted."

"Wait," said the head man of the village, "we can frighten the moon away. Let us throw stones and rocks at her, and that will surely frighten her and she will not burn our fine crops."

All the men and women ran every which way to find rocks, and then they threw them at the moon. They kept on throwing rocks all the time.

"Don't stop," the chief kept on shouting. "Let us keep on frightening that moon away until morning, when we will know our crops are safe."

And this is what they did. They kept on throwing rocks at the moon until the sun was in the sky and the moon had faded away.

15. LIKE MASTER, LIKE SERVANT

(China)

There lived in China in the old days a very silly scholar named Ping Sin, who had a most silly servant named Pu Shih. One was never seen without the other, and wherever the two were seen, people wondered which of the two was the sillier.

One day that silly scholar Ping Sin decided to take a walk in the shade along the river. He put on his boots, never noting that the two were different. One boot had a very thick sole, and the other a very thin one. Then he set out, his servant Pu Shih following behind. But soon Ping Sin found it difficult to walk. One foot would always sink down deeper than the other.

"I wonder what ails my feet today?" Ping Sin said.

75

"Perhaps the road is full of ruts from the recent rains."

A stranger, passing by, overheard the words.

"Venerable scholar Ping Sin," the stranger said, "there are no ruts in the road. There have been no rains here for many moons."

"Then why do my feet hurt and why are they forever going down unevenly?"

"Respected scholar Ping Sin, the reason is very simple. If you will look at the boots you are wearing, you will see that one is different from the other. One has a thick sole and the other has a thin sole. It is this difference that causes you discomfort. Change them for two same boots with the same kinds of soles, and you will find your walk very pleasant."

The scholar looked at his feet and found the stranger's words to be true. He turned to his servant and said, "Pu Shih, return to the house and bring me my other boots."

The servant turned his steps homeward and found the other boots. He examined them carefully. One had a very thick sole, the other a very thin one.

"Ah, these two are no better than those that my master Ping Sin already has on and which have brought him all this discomfort," thought the silly servant. "There is no use bringing these to my master—they are just as uneven as those he is wearing."

So he returned empty-handed to Ping Sin.

When the scholar saw him, he asked: "Pu Shih, where are the boots I asked you to bring me?"

"Honored master Ping Sin," he said, "I examined the boots you asked me to bring and found that they also had one thick sole and one thin sole. So there was no use bringing them to you."

"I am fortunate to have such a wise servant," the silly master said. "This day must be one of discomfort."

So he continued his walk with one thick sole and one thin sole.

16. THE SAD VICTORY

(China)

On a street in a city in China there lived a rich merchant. He had a beautiful home with fine gardens right in the middle of the street. His life would have been truly golden as plum blossoms if not for a never-ending din pounding in his ears from each end of the street.

For at one end was the dwelling of a blacksmith whose name was Yang Pu, and at the other end lived a coppersmith whose name was Yang Chu. From the first sound of the cock's crow until the last bird hid its head under its wing, the blacksmith hammered and banged away at knives and plows and other implements, while at the other end the coppersmith did the same on pots and pans. What was worse, both these fellows were noted sillies in the town, and so even when they had no work to do they would hammer and bang away to hear the earsplitting music of the noises.

All day the hammering banged in the merchant's ears like wild rivers in the spring floods, and the poor man suffered no end of misery. His head never stopped aching and he decided there must be some way to put an end to the never-ending din. He thought about it for a long time, and in the end he decided on a plan. He dressed himself in his green brocade robe with long sleeves and went to visit the blacksmith. The silly was busy banging away with his hammer, though he wasn't really making anything.

"Illustrious master blacksmith Yang Pu," the merchant began, "I suffer from a very grave illness in my ears that is made worse by your very important hammering. If you would like to bring health to me and gain to yourself, there is a very simple path."

"And what path is that?" the blacksmith asked.

"Find another place to do your endless hammering, and I will pay you well for it."

The blacksmith, who had little work and less to eat, gladly agreed when he heard the sum he would receive, and he promised to move away as soon as he could find a new place. The merchant told the blacksmith to come for the promised money as soon as he moved his shop.

Next the good merchant went to the house of the coppersmith Yang Chu. He found the silly fellow uselessly banging away, for there was neither kettle nor pot in the place. After the customary greetings, the merchant told the coppersmith what he had told the blacksmith—that he was ill, that the doctor had prescribed peace and silence as the only remedy, and that he was willing to pay a good price if the coppersmith would move to another house.

The coppersmith, like the blacksmith, earned just enough to keep skin and bones together. He was very glad indeed to be offered the good sum for just moving away, and so he quickly agreed.

The merchant went to his house happy at the great victory. Now, at last, he would have peace from the never-ending hammering of the silly craftsmen.

When the sun went on its well-beaten path behind the mountains, the blacksmith and the coppersmith, each going to the other's home to tell the good news, met in the middle of the road. Each related to the other his agreement with the merchant.

Both having kind hearts but little understanding, each wanted to please the merchant and earn the money. They discussed the matter and then Yang Pu the blacksmith said:

"I have a way out to please the honorable merchant and to bring us each the money he promised us."

"And what is it, honorable master?" Yang Chu the coppersmith asked.

"It is very simple. The merchant wants us each to move away from our homes and we will be well paid for it. Let me move into your house and you move into mine. Thus we will move as the merchant desires, and we will receive the money he promised us."

Since neither one nor the other had many possessions, it took them but little time to change their abodes, and then they both presented themselves to the merchant.

"I have moved my home and my workshop," said Yang Pu the blacksmith.

"And I have done the same," said Yang Chu the coppersmith, "and we have come for the money you promised us."

"Since you have both done as I asked you," the merchant said, "you have both earned the money I promised. Here it is," and he counted out to each the amount he had promised, and they both left, well satisfied, even as was the merchant.

The next morning, there was the banging and hammering as usual! The merchant rushed to the right end of the street where the blacksmith used to be, and there was the coppersmith hammering away louder than ever.

"What are you doing here?" the merchant cried.

"I moved, as I told you, from that end of the street to this end."

The merchant rushed to the left end of the street where the coppersmith used to be, and there was the blacksmith making enough noise to wake those in the upper regions.

"What are you doing here?" the distraught merchant cried.

"I moved away, as you asked me, to this place. I moved from my end of the street to this end."

What could the merchant say or what could the merchant do? He just remembered the proverb he had heard from a wise man: "It is easier to put your little finger through a thick stone than to put sense into a stupid head."

The next morning, there was the banging and hammering as usual!

17. WHEN NOODLEHEAD MARRIES NOODLEHEAD

(Africa)

In the northern part of Africa, not far from Arabia, there lived a silly young fellow who married a silly young girl. Since they were alike in everything, they were happy.

One day the silly young wife said to the silly young husband:

"I want some butter. We have none in our hut, so go to my father and mother and ask them to give you some."

"I would like some good butter, too," said the silly young husband. "I will go."

He took a wooden bowl and went through the woods until he came to his wife's parents' hut.

"Your fine daughter, who is now my good wife, would like some butter. We have none in the house so she sent me here to ask you to give it to us."

The mother said, "Good, I have plenty of butter. Give me your bowl and I will fill it."

He gave her the bowl, and she filled it with butter. Thanking her, he turned back into the woods to go home. After walking a distance, he came to an open field where the sun had dried and parched a piece of land so that it looked gray and barren.

"Poor piece of land," the silly fellow said, "you look so dry and hungry. Food will do you good. This is the land where I was born, and it is my duty to feed you. I'll give you plenty of butter, and it will make you strong and green."

He took the butter and smeared it carefully on the dry brown grass. He smeared it and smeared it until there was nothing left in his bowl. Then he went home, happy and smiling.

The wife saw the bowl, but no butter in it.

"Where is the butter, husband?" the young wife asked.

"Wife," he said, "on the way I saw a piece of our land dry and starved. It is our land and the land of our fathers. So I gave it the butter your mother gave me."

"That was the right thing to do, but when my

mother hears it, she will be angry. Let us go from here."

"Good," said the husband. "Let us pack some things and the flour we ground to feed us."

They did this, and soon they were on their way through the forests and fields. They walked for a long time until they were tired and hungry. In the distance there was a green lake.

"Let us go to that lake and sit down and rest ourselves and eat," the young wife said.

"Good," said the husband.

They came to the lake and sat down.

"There is shade here and it is cool. It is a fine place to rest and eat, wife."

"It couldn't be better, husband. It is just what we need. There is water here and the sun burns hot. The lake will be our pot and the sun our fire."

"You are a wise woman," the husband said.

She threw the flour into the lake.

"Now I must stir it well, so there are no lumps in it. I'll stir it with a stirring stick."

She took the stick and jumped into the lake. The lake was deep, deep, and she went down, down—and did not come up.

The young husband waited and waited.

"Ah, that is not nice. There is my wife down there

eating the meal without lumps, never asking me to join her. Soon there'll be nothing for me. I will join her."

So he jumped into the middle of the lake. The lake was deep, deep, and he went down, down—and did not come up.

You can guess what happened to those two sillies.

18. THE FOOLISH LION AND
THE SILLY ROOSTER

(Africa)

A long, long time ago there lived in the jungle of
Africa a silly lion whom the jungle people called Mnawika, and in the village nearby there lived a silly
rooster. The lion's den was near that village.

Early each morning the lion roared loud before the
sun rose. Soon after, the cock crowed "Konkolegu," and
then the sun came over the trees.

"Who dares make a noise like me?" roared Mnawika.

No one answered, so the lion called the bird Dudui
to go to find out who dared make a noise like the King
of the Jungle.

Dudui flew to the village and saw the rooster strut-
ting around and crowing.

"Was it you who imitated Mnawika?"

"Yes, it was I who made a noise like a lion," said the cock proudly. "I am as great as the lion. They call me Sumba Mnaluli, and I am as great as an elephant."

So the Dudui bird flew to the lion and said:

"I found the one who made the noise like you. His name is Sumba Mnaluli, and he says he is as great as an elephant."

The lion roared angrily and pulled a hair from the mane on his neck.

"Dudui bird, take this to that insolent fellow and say this is a hair from the neck of Msengi Mnawika, the name by which they call me. I am the great roarer from afar."

Dudui took the hair and flew to the village where the cock lived and went to him.

"The great roarer from afar, Msengi Mnawika, plucked this hair from his neck and told me to give it to you. This will show you who he is."

The cock flew to the top of the house, pulled from his neck a feather that was wider than the lion's hair, and gave it to the Dudui bird and said:

"Here, give this greeting from me to the lion. Tell him it is a hair from the neck of Sumba Mnaluli. You can see it is a much wider hair than the lion's."

The Dudui bird took the feather and flew back to the lion.

"O lion, Sumba Mnaluli sent you this hair from his neck and said it was wider than yours."

Again the lion roared in great anger, then he plucked the longest hair from his mane and said:

"Go back to that insolent fellow and show him this and tell him I have the strength of a hundred."

The Dudui bird took the hair and brought it straight to the rooster and said:

"The lion sent you this long hair and told me to tell you he has the strength of a hundred."

Sumba the cock looked at it and did not say a word. He raised his head proudly and plucked a long, long feather from his tail, maybe the longest, and gave it to the Dudui bird. He never said a word.

The Dudui bird carried it to the lion. When the lion saw that long feather, he just looked and did not say one word. He was silent and thought. Then he went and lay down to consider further. He said to himself: "Sumba is as great as an elephant, as you can judge from the size of his hair. I must know this important person." Then he went to sleep.

Very early the next morning the lion went to the village to see Sumba Mnaluli, the rooster.

It was very early, and the cock flew up to the very top of the house and crowed at the top of his voice: "I am Sumba Mnaluli, I am Sumba Mnaluli."

Right then the lion came up and saw the crowing

cock on top of the house. It was still a little dark, and the house looked as if it were the rooster's body.

The lion looked long and said, "Truly he is as great as an elephant."

He was frightened and tried to run away, but the people of the village were awake and saw him and captured him.

19. WHO IS WHO?

(Persia)

Once there was a great wrestler in Persia who lived in a deep wood. His muscles were strong as mountains, and sometimes, just for practice, he would wrestle with hundred-year-old trees and pull them out of the earth as if they were feathers. But in his mind, a drop of understanding would have been a deluge—he was such a Noodlehead!

All his life this wrestler lived in the forest, but one day he decided to go to the great capital and match his strength against the famous wrestlers there. He set off on the road, a heavy stick in his hand.

As he came nearer to the great capital of Persia, the people on the road grew larger in numbers. To the wrestler, it seemed like thousands upon thousands He was not used to seeing such a great crowd and he was frightened.

"Never have I seen so many people. I wonder from where they all come? Do the people of the whole world go to Teheran? Allah! I will surely get lost. I am sure I will not know myself if I have not something about me that others have not."

A man, selling yellow pumpkins, passed by, and the wrestler bought one of them. Then he tied it on a string to his right leg and, so decorated, came into the great city of Teheran.

He walked about the streets, and a young man saw him with the pumpkin tied to his leg.

"Whither to, friend?" he asked. "And why have you a pumpkin tied to your leg?"

"I am a great wrestler and I have come to match myself against the wrestlers of the capital of our land."

"But you did not tell me why you have this pumpkin tied to your leg."

"There are so many people here, I am afraid I will not know myself among them, so I tied the pumpkin to my leg to make certain I will recognize myself."

The young Persian knew at once that he was dealing with a man from Hums, the city in the East where fools came from, and so, hoping to have some sport with him, he said:

"Come to my house as my guest and you can stay there until you find some wrestlers to match your strength."

"May Allah favor you in your dealings for your generosity and hospitality. I will gladly go with you." He followed the young man to his home, where they ate and made good cheer. Then the wrestler went to sleep.

The young Persian, who liked a good jest, untied the pumpkin from his guest's leg and tied it to his own and also went to sleep.

Early in the morning, with the rising of the sun, the wrestler arose. He washed himself and prayed, and then he noticed that his leg had no pumpkin tied to it. He rushed back into the sleeping room where his host was still in the bed and—there was the pumpkin, tied to *his* leg!

He looked and looked in great surprise. This was strange. Was he, the wrestler, still in bed? The pumpkin was the proof! Trying to figure out the matter, he cried:

"Ho there, host, arise! I am deeply perplexed. Who am I and who are you? The pumpkin is gone from my leg and is on yours.

"If I am myself, why isn't the pumpkin on my leg? And if you are yourself, why is that pumpkin on your leg?"

The answers and the arguments are not told in the tale, but you can surely guess them for yourself. Perhaps when the host saw how disturbed his guest was, he told him of the joke. Let us hope he did, for one should be kind to foolish people.

20. MAGIC! SILLY MAGIC!

(Japan)

Mukashi, mukashi, long, long ago there were two brothers. One was very smart and the other was very silly. Sankuro, the older brother, was the Noodlehead, but he was very rich; Takuro, the younger, was the rogue, but he was poor.

One day Takuro, the rogue, was boiling water for his tea in an old rusty kettle over a little fire. Soon the kettle was singing, and the water boiled over. Takuro took the kettle off the fire quickly and put it on the floor, where it kept on boiling, as kettles always do for a time even after they are taken off the fire.

Now, it happened that right at that moment Sankuro, the silly one, entered the room to visit his brother. He saw the old kettle standing on the floor and boiling.

"*Ohio gozarimasu* [good morning]," said Takuro.

"*O tenki* [It's a fine day]," answered Brother Sankuro. "What is that I see? A kettle boiling on the ground without fire under it! I never saw anything like it."

"No you have not, Brother Sankuro. This is a magic kettle. It boils water without fire. It was my good fortune to get it from an old man."

"I would like to possess that tea kettle," said Sankuro, who was not only very silly but very greedy, as such people often are.

"Honorable elder brother," said Takuro, "I do not like to sell this kettle."

"But I want it very much," said Sankuro, "and I will pay you well for it."

He kept on begging, and in the end Takuro sold it to him for a good price and Sankuro, the silly, went home well pleased, saying, "*Sayonara* [Good-by]."

No sooner had Sankuro come to his house than he asked his servant to scrub and clean and polish the kettle until it shone like new money. Then he filled it with water, put it on the floor in the middle of the room, and sat down nearby to watch it. He waited and he waited, but the kettle just stood—that's all. The water never boiled. This made Sankuro very angry, and he ran to his brother at once and shouted:

"The kettle you sold me doesn't boil water without fire! I waited a long time, and the water is still standing there—cold, just the way I put it on."

"Honorable elder brother, what did you do to the kettle when you brought it to your home?"

"I had my servant clean it and scrub it and polish it until it shone bright. Then I put in water and set it on the ground to boil," answered Sankuro, the silly one.

"Oh, honorable elder brother, you did something very wrong. You scrubbed and polished the kettle, and you should never have done that. You scrubbed and polished away the magic, and you made it the same as any other kettle. It lost its magic. Had you left it alone, it would have boiled for you just as it did for me."

What could Sankuro say? He was too silly to say anything!

21. THE FARMER'S SECRET

(Japan)

A long time ago there lived in Japan a very silly farmer. You could tell him any flowery tale and he would believe it.

One day he was working in his garden, plowing and digging the black earth and planting yellow seeds.

A man walked by carrying a basket. He stopped and looked at the farmer for a long time, then he said:

"Ohio, gozarimasu [Good morning]."

The farmer did not answer.

After a time the man watching spoke again and said: *"O tenki* [It's a fine day]."

The farmer did not answer.

"What are you planting there, good friend?" the man said again.

The farmer just glanced at him and then went on with his work. When the man looking on did not go away, the farmer motioned him with his hand to come closer, which he did.

The man said:

"Why didn't you answer my greeting? Why don't you talk? You should be polite to strangers."

The old farmer straightened up and motioned the man to come closer. When he was right next to him, the farmer put his mouth close to the stranger's ear and whispered:

"Forgive me for my rudeness. I did not mean to be impolite. I am planting beans."

"You say you are planting beans! What is the great secret about that? Everybody plants beans."

"Sh . . . Not so loud! The pigeons are forever eating the seeds I plant, and if I spoke out loud they might hear what I said and come flying to eat the seeds. That is why I did not answer you."

The man just looked at that silly farmer, then he walked off. That's all.

22. THE WISDOM OF THE LORD

(Turkey)

Many years ago there lived in Turkey a hodja, a beloved teacher by the name of Nasr-ed-Din, who was very famous because he made people laugh. He was a short, fat fellow with a round face that was always smiling. On his nose sat big eyeglasses, and when he rode on a donkey he always carried his bag in his hand—so it wouldn't weigh down the poor beast, he would say.

Young people and old people loved him because he was always joking and laughing and doing the funniest and wisest and silliest things in the world. It was really hard to tell whether he was a Noodlehead or a wise teacher. When folks asked him, he would answer with an old proverb: "Fools and Noodleheads often give good advice."

One day he was busy in his garden. He hoed the black earth, and then he weeded around the vegetables and vines. After that he raked the ground around the green cabbages and the purple eggplants. He hilled the corn and took away the grass that grew between the cucumbers and rows of watermelons. Then, after he finished taking care of his vegetables, he turned to tilling the ground around his roses and geraniums, and around his honeysuckle vines.

When all this was done, the hodja sat down under a tall leafy nut tree that stood in the middle of the garden. Leaning against the trunk, he looked at the fine, healthy vegetables and plants and at the beautiful sweet-smelling flowers. Next he looked up into the sunny sky where little clouds were chasing one another. Then his eyes ran over to his tall nut tree, full of nuts hanging between swinging, glossy leaves.

As the hodja looked up at the tree full of fruit he cried out, "O, mighty Lord of heaven! Sometimes I wonder about Your wisdom. Some of the things You do seem different from what they should be. There on the ground is a vine You have created. It is as thin as my little finger, and on it are growing watermelons twice as big as my head.

"At the same time, on that great strong tree that is

twice as big as my body, there grow nuts not as big as my thumb. It would seem to me the big, thick watermelons should hang on the big, thick tree and that the little nuts should grow on the slender vines. That is the way I would have arranged the plants, O Lord of the world."

At that moment a warm wind raced through the air and shook the leaves of the tree, and one of the green nuts fell right on the hodja, hitting him lightly on the nose. He was startled and silent for just a moment; then a smile came over his face.

"O Lord of the universe!" he cried. "What a silly fellow am I, and how wise You are. If a watermelon had been on that tree and had fallen on me, it surely would have broken not only my nose but my teeth as well, and maybe my whole face. No wonder people call me silly and laugh at me."

23. THE COSTLY FEAST

(Turkey)

Once this famous hodja received a young lamb from a distant rich relative. The good teacher was very happy, for he knew it was a gift from the heart. He fed the little animal and gave it plenty of water, but neighbors, friends, and relatives looked with big eyes on that lamb. They wanted to see it in their stomachs, not in the green pasture. Since greed has long arms, they were scheming how to get the hodja to butcher it for their benefit so they would have a feast without paying for it.

Now, it was well known that the hodja was a man with a very simple head who believed almost anything you told him. One morning a large number of these false friends came to him and said:

"Oh, Hodja, it would be wise for you to slaughter your lamb."

"And why should I do this," said he, "when I can wait and let it grow up to twice its size?"

"Don't you know?" they all cried. "A terrible thing is about to happen in three days!"

"What terrible thing will happen in three days?"

"We will all go to Paradise. The world is coming to an end," they cried.

"I did not know that."

"That is why we came to tell it to you. It would be wiser for you to slaughter your lamb at once and eat it while you can."

"I will do that, good friends," the hodja said. "Tomorrow I will slaughter it, and you can come and enjoy the feast with me."

They praised and thanked him and said to him:

"You are a good man who believes in Allah. For you follow the words: 'When Allah gives, he does not ask whose son art thou.'" But secretly they said, "Fools make feasts and wise men eat."

The next day friends, relatives, and even strangers came like locusts to enjoy the free feast. The lamb was prepared and put on the spit for roasting. Then they all sat down to wait.

Now, it was a very hot day and the company felt warm. So they took off their clothes and went to sleep

"Why not use the clothes?" said the hodja. *"They will not need them by tomorrow."*

under the shade of the trees while the hodja remained at the spit to watch the meat get well roasted. But the fire began to die down, and the hodja looked around for wood to keep the flame going. There was no wood near, only the clothes of the sleeping friends.

"Why not use the clothes?" said the hodja. "They will not need them by tomorrow."

He took the sleepers' clothes and fed the fire with them. One bundle after another went up in the flames to roast the lamb on the spit. When all the clothes were burned, the lamb looked crisp and brown and well done.

The sun was low, and one after another the company awoke for the feast. They began looking for their clothes but none could find them.

"Where are our clothes?" one and another shouted. "Did you see anyone take them, Hodja? We left them here in bundles."

"No one took them, good friends," the hodja replied. "True, you left your clothes here, but I took them, one bundle after another, and used them to feed the fire so the lamb would be well roasted."

"Fool of fools! Was ever such a fool in our land? True are the words: 'A fool throws a stone into the sea and forty wise men can't get it out.' Don't you know that we need our clothes?"

"But, good friends, what need have you of your

clothes? Didn't you say that tomorrow the world would be coming to an end and we would all be in Paradise?"

What could they say? For once they were not sure who was the fool, the hodja or they, so they just feasted on the lamb. And a costly feast it was!

24. THE FLYING FOOL

(South America)

In South America there once lived a man who had a father and a mother and a sister. They were just like other people, but not that man—he had no sense in his head. For that reason they called him Wabassi, which means a man who is not quite right in the head. His sister had a fine dog named Warribisi.

One day Wabassi went to the seashore to catch crabs. Just as he was getting into the boat a big jaguar came toward him. Being a silly fellow, Wabassi thought it was his sister's dog.

"Come here, Warribisi; come here, Warribisi. What are you doing on the seashore? Come with me."

He tried to pull the dog into the boat, but the jaguar clawed and bit him.

"Don't bite and growl, Warribisi. Be a nice dog."

But the jaguar wouldn't come, and he was too heavy to be carried. Wabassi became angry and cried:

"You fool of a dog, if you don't want to come along, stay where you are. I hope a jaguar comes along and eats you. Then you will know better."

He went about his business. When he was done, he went home. There he told what had happened to him.

"Sister, I saw your dog by the sea."

"That could not be, brother. My dog was with me all the time. You are silly and see all kinds of things that aren't."

"I wonder what it could have been," Wabassi said.

A week later, Wabassi went out hunting with the men of the village. Soon they found a herd of wild pigs. The pigs ran in all directions, and the men ran after them, shooting. So did Wabassi.

The men gathered the pigs they had shot and put them all in one place. But there was no Wabassi. Soon he came.

"Where were you?" they cried.

"I was shooting at wild pigs way off in the woods, and I shot one. But it does not look like the pigs you shot. It has spots and a flat nose."

"We never saw such a pig," the hunters said. "Bring it here. We would like to see it."

He went and soon came back, dragging his "pig" behind. What do you think it was? It was a . . . jaguar!

"Only fools have such luck! You shot a jaguar."

"The beast never scratched me."

"We couldn't do that if we tried," the hunters cried.

Then they all went home and had a fine feast, and Wabassi was very proud of himself.

"Look what I can do," he said to his sister. "I can do anything."

The next morning he rose early, still feeling very proud. He walked out in the woods and saw the birds flying.

"I can fly like a bird if I want to," he thought.

He put on clothes of many colors, like a bird, and stuck feathers in his belt, front and back. Then he climbed high up in a tree and leaped from branch to branch.

"There! I can fly like a bird if I want to. Sister, sister, come out! Watch me fly like a bird."

His sister came. Right then Wabassi jumped on a branch that was thin and dry and fell down from on high. He was in great pain, but do you think he cried?

Not Wabassi, the fool! He rubbed himself all over and said:

"Didn't I fly as fine as any bird? No one in the village can do that. Only I."

25. THE WISE MEN OF GOTHAM

(England)

THREE OF A KIND

Who hasn't heard of the merry men of Gotham in England? Some call them "the wise men of Gotham," for they solved the hardest problems to their own good satisfaction and to the laughing joy of the rest of England. There is no land where their tales are not told, and folks, young and old, find pleasure in hearing them and telling them. And so I shall tell you some.

There were two men of Gotham, and one of them was going to Nottingham to buy sheep and the other was coming from the market of that city, and both met on Nottingham bridge.

"Well met," said the one going to Nottingham.

"Whither are you a-going?" said he that came from Nottingham.

"Marry," said he that was going thither, "I am going to the market to buy sheep."

"Buy sheep," said the other. "And which way will you drive them home?"

"Marry," said the other, "I will bring them over this bridge."

"By Robin Hood," said he that came from Nottingham, "but thou shalt not."

"By Maid Marion," said he that was going thither, "but I will."

"Thou shalt not," said the one.

"I will," said the other.

Then each raised his stave threateningly—not beating it upon the other's head, but against the ground, one against the other as if there really had been a hundred sheep betwixt them.

"Hold those sheep there!" cried the one.

"Beware of the leaping over the bridge of my sheep," said the other.

"They shall not go over this bridge," said the one.

"They shall come over this very bridge," said the other.

"But they shall not," said the one.

And they kept arguing and arguing whether the

sheep were to go over the bridge or not, though there were no sheep there at all.

As they were in this foolish contention, another wise man from Gotham came from the market with a sack of meal upon his horse. Seeing and hearing his neighbors at strife about sheep that were not there, he said:

"Ah, fools, will you never learn wit? Let me teach it to you and show you how much sense there is in your noodles. Come, help me," said he that had the meal, "and put this sack upon my shoulders."

They did so, and he went to one side of the bridge and unloosed the mouth of his sack and shook out the meal into the river.

Then he said:

"How much meal is there in the sack, neighbors?"

"Marry," answered they. "None."

"Now, by my faith," answered the wise man of Gotham, "even so much wit is there in your two heads to battle for a thing you have not."

Now, which was the worst Noodlehead of these three persons? I leave you to judge.

CUCKOO IN THE HEDGE

The men of Gotham and their wives and children all loved the singing of the birds in the green. Above all, they loved the cuckoo who sang first when the springtime came and it was no longer cold and dour.

So the men of Gotham wanted to keep the cuckoo well enclosed so that it would sing for them all year long.

In time they made a round wall of stout wood right in the middle of the town, but they forgot to put a roof on it. Then they got a cuckoo and put her into it and said:

"Sing here for us all the year and thou shalt lack neither meat nor drink. And it will give all of us much joy."

The cuckoo, as soon as she saw that she was encompassed within the hedge, flew away through the top of it.

The men of Gotham saw her rise in the air and they said:

"A vengeance on her! We made not our hedge high enough."

26. THE BRAVE MEN OF AUSTWICK

(England)

You have heard of the men of Gotham and the way they solved all their problems, but have you heard of the men of Austwick in Yorkshire in England? The carls, as men were called in the olden days, were trying to outdo the men of Gotham, and oft as not it was hard to tell who were the bigger Noodleheads.

Now, the men, or carls, of Austwick had only one knife or whittle in their town, for steel and iron cost much in those days. So the whole town used the one whittle, which was kept under a tree. Whenever it was in use and another wanted it, he'd call out, "whittle to the tree," and then the one who had it would bring it back to the tree.

So everyone had the use of that knife for a long time.

One day a few Austwick men went working in the moor and took the whittle with them to cut their bread and cheese.

They worked all day but did not finish, and so had to return the next day.

"Why not leave the whittle here till the morrow? Then we'll not have to carry it all the way home, or bring it all the way here tomorrow," one said.

They all said aye to this.

"But we must put it in a place we'll remember," spoke one.

On this, too, they agreed.

"Let us find a spot we'll not forget."

They began to look about.

A thick, black cloud in the sky cast a dark shadow on the green grass near a tree and they saw the black spot.

"Let us put it on this black spot that is on the grass. We are sure to find it when we come again."

So the knife was stuck in the middle of the black shadow on the ground, and then the men went home, contented with their task.

The next morning they came to the moor to start work again, and when the noon hour came they sat down to eat their meal.

Said one: "Let us get our whittle to cut our bread

and cheese. I'll go fetch it from the middle of the black spot where we left it yesterday."

He went to the place, but the cloud in the sky was no longer where it had been, and there was no black spot to be found anywhere, search as he would.

They could not find the whittle any place, so they ate their cheese and bread without cutting it, and when the sun began to set, turned homeward to tell the sad news.

Then the carls of Austwick had to save their money a long time before they could buy another whittle.

27. KNUCKLEHEAD JOHN

(England)

In Merrie England there were not only Noodleheads, but Knuckleheads as well. And what is a Knucklehead? Well, it's about the same as a Noodlehead.

In England, I knew a soldier and he told me many Knucklehead stories, and now I will tell you some of them.

There was, in a company of cavalry, a real Knucklehead, who was forever forgetting what he was told to do, and what he remembered, he did wrong. Everyone called him Knucklehead John.

One day the corporal said, "John, go and saddle my horse and bring it out in front of the barracks."

Knucklehead John went to the stall, got the corporal's horse, and worked for a long time with the saddle. When he was done, he had put on the saddle with the front toward the back. He led the horse out in front of the barracks.

When the company saw it, they all laughed.

"What in the world did you do with that saddle?" asked the corporal.

"I put it on."

"So you did, but you put the front side backwards."

"Don't worry, corporal," Knucklehead John said smilingly. "It will be all right. Just you turn the horse around when you ride."

No one said a word after that!

Soon after, Knucklehead John was out on a march, a full, loaded knapsack on his back. The sack was full of the things a soldier needs on a march, and it was very heavy and pressed hard on his shoulders. It hurt most right in the center.

"This kit weighs heavy on my shoulders, and it is getting heavier with every step I take. I wish it weren't so hard on me," John said to the soldier walking next to him.

The fellow knew Knucklehead John, as did everyone else in the company.

"That load would be less heavy if you had it properly balanced," he said.

"Isn't it properly balanced?"

"It is not. It presses hard on the middle of your shoulders all the time, which is a very bad place. Now, if you put one pack on one shoulder and another on the other shoulder to balance it, it would weigh much less."

Knucklehead John thought this was a fine idea, so he put his own knapsack on one shoulder while the soldier loaded his own kit on John's other shoulder. John walked along with both loads weighing him down worse than before. When the march was over, the soldier who had loaded his knapsack on John's back asked:

"How did you fare, John?"

"I didn't feel a pain on the middle of my shoulders," said Knucklehead John. "I felt it all over. That was much, much easier."

"If you put one pack on each shoulder, it will weigh less."

28. A SHEEP CAN ONLY BLEAT

(Scotland)

There was once a man who lived in Scotland who had as little sense as would go into a sparrow's egg—and at that, it would sure have to be a small egg. His wife had a hard time of it, but she did the best she could, saying:

"There are vices worse than foolishness, and 'tis well known that bairns and dogs love fools. Then why shouldn't I?"

One day the woman said to the man—his name was Ian:

"Ian, my spinning wheel is broken and needs mending. You take it to town and have it done. When you're on the road, ride fair and bespatter no one, and with the help o' God, you'll get there without mishap."

The man went to the town and had the spinning wheel fixed properly. Then he put it on his back and began walking home.

He walked and he walked, greeting those who passed him and thinking of the good meal he'd find on the table.

He walked and he walked, slowly, for the wheel was beginning to weigh heavy on his back.

"I wonder how 'tis," said he aloud to himself, "I wonder how 'tis that a load grows heavier the longer it's on your back. Maybe it gets bigger in the walking, or maybe the air weighs it down harder with every step. My back is aching worse every minute."

The wind came up from the purple heather, setting the wheel whirring and running.

"Mercy me!" cried Ian, stopping, "there's a wonderful thing! A spinning wheel running of its own power without the help of any woman's foot!

"Well, my good magic spinning wheel, if you can spin by yourself, you can spin yourself home—and under your own power to the house. You know the place well enough. You've been there plenty of years."

He let the wheel down off his aching back.

"Now, get home, my friend. I'll see you there in good time."

Then he turned home, feeling much better without

the load. When he got to the door, he asked his wife if the spinning wheel had arrived.

"No spinning wheel came," quoth she. "I thought 'twas you who was to bring it home."

"If it didn't come home, then it sure must have taken a shorter road," said Ian.

"Didn't you bring it home after having it mended?" she asked.

"I carried it halfway," said Ian. "Then it began spinning by itself. Now, a spinning wheel that can spin by itself surely can walk home by itself. So I set it on the ground and let it walk home."

"Merciful Lord," cried she, "what can you expect from a sheep, save bleating?" And she ran out to look for the spinning wheel.

29. A NEW WAY TO BOIL EGGS

(Ireland)

There was a man lived in Ireland who had so many brains in his head, he tried one day to milk a duck. This man had a wife, and she had the same kind of feathers in her head as her husband had.

The two lived in a small cottage on a small strip of land. On the land they had a hen house made from old boxes and bits of tin they had found. It wasn't much of a hen house, but enough to hold four hens that weren't bad layers, with the help of the Lord.

The hens were laying eggs, and the Lynches—that was their name—were eating them.

Now, Johnny Lynch, he loved boiled eggs. He said they had a fine, soft flavor, but he had no liking at all for any other kinds of cooked eggs, like scrambled or fried. But his wife, Bridget, she loved her eggs scrambled or fried only—best of all when they were fried with a bit of bacon. She couldn't stand the taste of boiled eggs—they were too slithery, she said. Johnny, he couldn't stand fried eggs—they were too smelly, he said. There wasn't much agreement between these two. But you know, ask a woman once or twice, and if she doesn't change, you might as well give in.

Johnny, he was just losing his mind smelling fried bacon and eggs. The more he argued with Bridget about it, the more she said she'd eat them dead or alive.

So Johnny, he began using his head overtime, trying to figure out how to break the bone of contention in his house.

One day he thought to himself: "If only I could train them hens to lay boiled eggs, that'd fix the old woman, all right!" One afternoon, he had an inspiration.

He waited till Bridget had gone to a neighbor; then he took a kettle full of water and put it on the fire and let it heat until it was boiling hard. And when the water was boiling, he took it to the hen house and put it in an empty watering pan that was standing in the corner. The hens, seeing it, rushed over at once to drink.

"Oh, just ye drink that hot water and ye'll be sure to lay boiled eggs."

Every time Bridget was away gossiping, Johnny took boiling water to the chickens in the hen house. Then he waited for the chickens to lay boiled eggs.

Did they lay boiled eggs after drinking the boiled water?

Oh, musha, I can't tell exactly. I wasn't there when the hens laid eggs after drinking the hot water.

30. THE NEEDLE CROP OF SAINTE-DODO

(France)

The folks of Sainte-Dodo! They were famous throughout the land for the words they spoke and the deeds they did, and all France laughed at them. In fact, they were so famous that if someone in that country did something silly, it was said he must come from Sainte-Dodo.

They worked in their village just as people worked in other villages—that is, plowing the land and harvesting whatever grew. And plowing was hard and waiting for things to grow was long, and they were poorly paid in the end. So they were not too happy, and the elders thought something should be done about bettering their lot in the world.

Everyone—men, women, and children—came to the front of the church where they met to discuss problems.

"Folks of Sainte-Dodo," said the oldest of the Sainte-Dodonians, "we work hard and get less than most people in Gascogne. Therefore we must find a way to work less and get more than most people."

Everybody thought that was a fine idea.

"I have thought of a way," the old farmer went on. "You know everybody needs needles all the time. They are scarce and they cost many francs. My wife just asked for a second one this year. Just think of that! Why don't we grow needles and earn much money that way? The needles will grow—weeds or no weeds—so we won't have to work in the fields all the time. We can sit back and wait while they grow. When the proper time comes, we will harvest them and sell them at a good price."

"All France needs needles," the women said.

"Let us send three strong men to Toulouse to buy a bag of needles and then we will sow them," the mayor said.

So it was done, and in good time the three strong men returned with a small sack of needles.

The needles were sown in the earth, and everybody was happy.

After ten days, the major of Sainte-Dodo said:

"Let us go to the fields and see if the needle-seeds

have sprouted. But we must take our shoes off lest we crush the tender little seedlings."

The shoes went off, and in bare or stockinged feet the whole village went to the field where the sowing was done to see if the needle seeds had come up.

As the good citizens of Sainte-Dodo walked on the field, the needles stuck into their bare feet.

"Ah," they cried with joy, "we feel the sticky sprouts of the needles. There will be a fine crop of needles, and we will be paid many francs. We don't have to weed, either—the needles will take care of that."

Everybody went home and waited day after day for the needle crop. Neighbors far and wide were told about the needles that were growing—and everybody laughed about it.

But the good Sainte-Dodonians just sat back and waited, and maybe they are waiting to this very day!

31. BAHHH!

(France)

More than a thousand years ago, there lived in France a numskull, a Noodlehead-shepherd. His name was Lamkin. He was so silly he'd scold the grass in the springtime because it did not grow fast enough.

He watched his flock day and night, but got paid little for his pains by his master, William the Draper. So whenever he was very hungry, he would take a young lamb from the flock and make a good meal of it.

But one day his master William caught him at the game and told him he'd have to come before the judge to be punished. Lamkin did not like this at all, but there was no way out, so to the village he went on court day.

Now, Lamkin knew that one needed a lawyer to

come before a judge, so he found Pierre Patelin, who was the lawyer in the village. Folks said he was smart as a cuckoo.

"M-m-m-Master P-p-p-Patelin," he said, stuttering as he always did, "I am in t-t-trouble."

"What's your trouble?" Patelin asked.

"I m-m-m-must come before th-th-the judge."

"Why do you have to come before the judge?"

"M-m-m-Master says I took his sh-sh-sh-sheep and didn't p-p-p-pay. He d-d-didn't give me enough to eat. I was hungry."

"You are in great trouble, Friend Lamkin, in great trouble."

"I know I am. Wh-wh-what should I do?"

"I'll tell you what to do, but you must pay me well for the advice."

"I h-h-h-have five c-c-crowns that I saved for f-f-f-five years."

"That will be the right amount and I promise you'll go free. Just do what I tell you."

"Wh-wh-what should I do?"

"Do nothing, that's all."

"D-d-d-do nothing?"

"Yes, just do nothing. When anyone asks you anything—when the judge speaks to you, when your master, William, speaks to you—just answer with one word: 'Bahhh!' "

"B-b-b-bahhh?" Lamkin bleated.

"Yes—bahhh! When anybody speaks to you—it does not matter who—just say the one word: 'Bahhh!' "

"B-b-b-bahhh!" Lamkin bleated again.

"That's what I said—Bahhh!—to everything the judge or anybody else says."

"H-h-ho, th-th-th-that's easy, M-m-m-Master Patelin. I'll say it t-t-t-to everybody al-all right!"

"Remember that and remember the five crowns."

"I w-w-won't forget!"

The judge came and so did the bailiff. So did Lamkin, Patelin, and Master William, the Draper.

Master William spoke first:

"Your Lordship, that shepherd, Lamkin, took my sheep and ate them and never paid for them."

The judge had a grim face.

"Did you take the sheep, Lamkin, without paying for them?"

"B-b-b-Bahhh!" bleated Lamkin.

"What did you say? I asked you, did you take sheep from your master, William? Answer me!"

"B-b-b-Bahhh!"

"Are you crazy?" the judge cried. "I asked you a question. Answer!"

"B-b-b-Bahhh!"

"Is this fellow an idiot, Master William? Is that the kind of shepherd you have to watch your sheep?"

"B-b-b-Bahhh!" Lamkin bleated.

"He is an idiot, all right, your Lordship, but he can speak. He stole those sheep and never paid for them. He can speak. You took my sheep, didn't you?"

"B-b-b-Bahhh!"

The judge was so angry he was red in his face.

"Out of my sight," he screamed. "I have no time for Noodleheads. I never want to see you again. You, Master William, are a fool for having such fools work for you. The court is dismissed!" and the judge went off in a huff.

Lamkin turned to leave, and Patelin followed him. When they were alone the lawyer said, "Wasn't it a fine idea, Lamkin? Now, my five crowns."

"B-b-b-Bahhh!" Lamkin bleated.

"Is that all I get for my work?" the lawyer asked.

"B-b-b-Bahhh," Lamkin bleated, and ran off. And that was all the lawyer ever got from that Noodlehead!

32. TALES FROM TARTARI-BARBARI

(France)

Cric! Crac! I'll tell you a story.

Knock, knock!

"Who's there?"

"It's me, sir."

"From where do you come, good friend?"

"I come from Tartari-Barbari, one hundred miles the other side of Paris."

"What did you see on the road, good fellow?"

"I saw a mill, high up on a tree, grinding flour."

"Noodlehead! That's stupid. Throw the fool into prison."

"Ho, inside!"

"Who's there?"

"It's me, sir."

"From where do you come, good friend?"

"I come from Tartari-Barbari, one hundred miles the other side of Paris."

"And what did you see on the way?"

"Oh, good sir, what didn't I see! I saw a black, shaggy dog limping down a high elm tree, his tail all covered with flour."

"Ah, good fellow, the dog must have swallowed some of the flour from that mill on the tree. Please let the poor fellow out of prison."

Knock, knock!

"Who's there?"

"I, good sir."

"From where do you come?"

"I come from Tartari-Barbari, one hundred miles this side of Paris."

"What did you see on the way, good fellow?"

"Oh, dear sir, what didn't I see! As I rode through Paris I saw a bird whose great wings covered the whole city."

"Phoo, that can't be true. It's foolish talk. You are just a Noodlehead. Throw the numskull into prison."

"Ho there, inside!"

"Who's there?"

"I, good sir."

"From where do you hail?"

"Good sir, I come from Tartari-Barbari, a hundred miles the other side of Paris."

"What did you see on the way, good friend?"

"What didn't I see, good sir! I saw a great crowd of people, thousands and thousands of them, with iron tongs in their hands, rolling a giant egg through the streets of Paris."

"Oh! Maybe that bird with the big wings laid that giant egg. Let the poor fellow out of prison."

Knock, knock!

"Who's there?"

"It's I, good sir."

"From where do you come?"

"From Tartari-Barbari, a hundred miles the other side of Paris."

"And what did you sight on the road, good friend?"

"I saw a big lake, and the water flowing in it was a mass of burning fire—just like dry straw."

"Numskull! Anyone with sense would know that wasn't true. Throw the foggyhead into prison."

Knock, knock!

"Who's there?"

"I, good sir."

"From where do you come, good friend?"

"Sir, I come from Tartari-Barbari, a hundred miles this side of Paris."

"And what did you see on the roads, my friend?"

"What didn't I see! I saw the strangest sight in all the world. Everywhere, in the meadows, in the fields, everywhere I saw carps and pikes running like mad, their tails burned to cinders."

"Oh! It must have been the fish from that burning stream. Let the poor fellow out of prison."

Knock, knock!

"Who's coming?"

"It's I, good sir."

"From where do you come, my friend?"

"Good sir, I come from Tartari-Barbari, a hundred miles this side of Paris."

"And what wonders did you see on the roads?"

"Oh, sir, what didn't I see! Holes and ditches, ruts and graves filled with mush. It was a great sight."

"Noodlehead! How can that be? Throw him into prison."

Knock, knock!

"Who's there?"

"I, good sir."

"From where do you come, friend?"

"Sir, I come from Tartari-Barbari, a hundred miles this side of Paris."

"What did you meet on the road, friend?"

"Oh, good sir, wherever I went, wherever I walked, I saw spoons of every shape and every kind of material—wood and tin, silver and gold, copper and brass."

"Oh, they were the spoons to be used for the mush in the holes and ditches, the ruts and the graves. Let this poor fellow out of prison."

My story is done!

33. PETER'S ADVENTURES

(Denmark)

There once lived a woman in Denmark who had a very foolish son. You couldn't match his silliness anywhere. They called him Peter the Fool, and he spent most of his day eating or sitting on the fence chewing dry straw.

One day his mother was busy churning, and soon she had a fine pot of butter.

"Mother, I want to go to town to sell the butter," said the Noodlehead.

"No, son, you better sit on the fence and keep the grass shady. You have never been to town and wouldn't know your way around."

"Mother, I want to see the town. I'll sell the butter for a good price."

He begged harder, but she said, "No." He begged still harder, and in the end she let him take the butter to sell.

Peter walked along the road, one, two, three, four; one, two, three, four. He walked a long time and came to a spot where a big stone lay in the middle of the road. He had never seen such a big stone.

"That must be the town," he said. "Good day, Mister Town."

No answer.

"Well, maybe you don't like talking. My mother always says too much talking killed a horse. I have a pot full of fine butter."

No answer.

"It's really the finest butter there ever was. If you don't believe me you can taste it."

He took a piece of butter, put it on a twig, and smeared it on the stone. The sun shone hot, the butter melted and was gone.

"Ah, you ate it fast. I don't blame you—it tastes fine. I'll sell it to you at a reasonable price," and he mentioned a sum.

No answer.

"The price is fair," Peter kept on, "and what's more,

you don't have to pay it right now, you can pay tomorrow."

No answer.

"My mother says silence is wiser than talking, and you believe that, too, I see. I will come back for the money tomorrow. I'll be here at the same time. Here is the rest of the butter." He smeared the rest of the butter all over the big stone and then went home, well satisfied with the bargain he had made.

"Son, did you sell the butter?" the mother asked.

"That I did, Mother. I sold it to the town and got a good price for it."

"Where is the money, son?"

"That I will get tomorrow."

"That's not a good way to do business."

"What is bad about it, Mother? You told me to go to town and sell the butter. I went to town and sold the butter and got the price I asked. I told the town I would come back tomorrow."

"Son, I can't make head or tail out of this. I should never have trusted you with selling. I hope you get your money tomorrow."

The next day came.

"Mother, I am ready to go to the town for the money."

"How can you get money from the town?"

"I will get it, Mother, don't fear."

She shrugged her shoulders and he went off down the road. Soon he came to the stone.

"I have come to get the money for the butter you bought from me yesterday," he said.

No answer.

"I gave you credit for one day only. Here I am. Where is the money?"

No answer.

"You better pay your debt. You ate that butter and owe me the money for it," silly Peter said, getting angry.

No answer.

The Noodlehead was so angry now, he was ready to burst.

"I trusted you with that money until today. Out with it!" he screamed.

No answer.

"I'll teach you!" Peter roared and began pushing and pummeling the stone with all his strength until he turned it over and it fell on its side. And there, right below, in a hole, was a pot filled with money!

"I see you are the kind who needs a hard argument before you pay," Peter said. He took the money and went home.

His mother opened her eyes wide when she saw the gold.

"Where did you get the money?" she cried.

"From the town. But I tell you, it wasn't easy. He's the kind that has to be pushed hard to pay. But I got the money in the end."

The mother took the money and said to herself, "Fortune often favors fools."

The week after, Peter's mother butchered a cow.

"Mother, give me some meat. I'll go and sell it to the town."

"You better not, son. You were lucky last time, but luck has a way of running out."

"I want to go, Mother. I am getting older, and I must learn to sell."

So the mother said he could go. She gave him a large piece of meat in a basket, and this time he really got to the town. Near the market there was a pack of dogs looking for scraps to eat. They smelled the meat and began barking and jumping around him.

"Good day," Peter said.

The dogs barked.

"Would you like to buy some fine fresh meat?"

The dogs barked, but to Peter it sounded like "Yes."

"The meat is very fresh. My mother butchered a cow two days ago. I'll sell it to you at a good price."

The dogs barked and jumped higher around him.

"I see you want to buy it. Would you like to taste it first?"

The dogs barked.

Peter cut off some pieces with his knife and threw them to the dogs.

They were gone before you could count three.

"I see you like it. Well, I want a gold piece for it."

The dogs barked and jumped higher.

"I see you agree," Peter said. "Since you struck the bargain so quickly, I will do for you what I did for the town the other day. You can pay me for it tomorrow. That's the way I do business."

The dogs barked.

"Fine," said Peter, and threw the meat among them. "I'll be here tomorrow at the same time to collect the money." Then he went home.

"Did you sell the meat?" the mother asked.

"Yes, Mother, I did."

"Where is the money?"

"I'll get it tomorrow, just as I did the last time."

The mother was satisfied, thinking of the pot of money her silly son had brought home before.

The next day Peter returned to the market, and the dogs were there.

"Did you like the meat?" Peter asked.

The dogs barked.

Said Peter: "Now, the money."

The dogs barked.

"Yes, I want my money now and don't try what that town tried."

The dogs barked and jumped.

"I have no meat now," Peter cried angrily. "I want the money for the meat I gave you yesterday. Pay or I'll teach you a lesson."

The dogs barked and jumped.

This made Peter angry, and he got hold of a small dog with a fine collar around his neck.

"You are the best dressed, so you must be the richest. You pay."

The dog barked and whined.

"You say no. Well, then, I'll take you before the king."

He went to the palace and asked the gatekeeper to see the king.

"If you pay me well, I'll let you see the king," the gatekeeper said.

"You are a dishonest fellow. One shouldn't pay for seeking justice, but if it's the only way, I promise you half of what I get," Peter answered.

The gatekeeper let him in, and Peter came to the king's door. There was the door guard, and he wouldn't let Peter go in.

"All I want is justice," cried Peter the Fool. "Let me in, and I'll give you the rest of what I get."

The guard let him walk in. There sat the king with a crown on his head, and next to him sat his lovely daughter with a very sad face. She never laughed, and the king had promised her in marriage to anyone who would make her laugh.

"Who are you?" the king asked.

"I am Peter the Fool, and I come to seek justice."

"What justice do you want?" the king asked.

Peter told the tale of how he had sold the meat to the dogs.

Said the king: "If you sold the meat to the dogs, you must collect the money from the dogs."

Peter was really angry now. He turned to the little dog he held under his arm, shook him, and cried:

"Do you hear what the king said? You must pay. Come on, I want my money."

The princess, who had been listening all the time, now began to laugh—for the first time in her life.

The king was so happy at this that he turned to Peter and said:

"Now, Peter, you don't have to worry about the money for your meat. You have made my daughter laugh, and now you can marry her and you will have all the money you want."

"I don't want to marry your daughter," Peter said.

"If you don't want to marry my daughter, I will give you a bag full of money instead."

"I don't want your money, either," Peter said.

"Well, what do you want?" the king said, growing angry.

"I want six strokes with a good whip."

"You want to be beaten?" the king cried. "You deserve it. Come, soldiers, give it to him."

"Not so fast, King. I promised half of what I got to the gatekeeper, who makes people pay before he lets them see you."

So the soldiers gave a beating to the gatekeeper.

Said Peter, when they were done:

"Now give the rest to your door guard, who plays the same dishonest trick. I promised the other half to him."

The door guard got his.

The princess laughed again.

"You have made my daughter laugh twice in one morning," the king said. "You can't be such a fool as people think. Marry my daughter. I think you will make a fine ruler."

"Now I will marry her," Peter said, "since the two guards who wanted to cheat me got theirs."

He married the princess, and for a Noodlehead he made a good king. He was not much worse than a smart one.

34. FAITHFUL LEGS AND
LAZY HEAD

(Gypsy)

If it hadn't happened, it wouldn't be told.

There was once a very silly gypsy. He was a
real Noodlehead: a silly, lazy know-nothing. He
couldn't sing and he couldn't dance; he couldn't play
a fiddle or a bass or a cymbalom; he couldn't mend
tins or cans and he had no horse or wagon. That's the
kind of gypsy he was.

Day and night he walked in the woods and through
the fields in clothes others threw away. If he hadn't
done a little work around farms and fields for a piece
of bread and a little straw to sleep on, he would have
starved and frozen.

He was walking along the road—tramp, tramp.

Like all gypsies, he believed he wouldn't die till he had swallowed a bushel of dust and a peck of dirt.

The sun shone hot and the wind blew strong and he felt very tired in his legs. He sat down on the green grass and looked at his legs. He said:

"You look tired, you faithful legs. You are as faithful as good dogs. You never fail me. You work all day long and carry me all over without complaining. Truly, you are very faithful."

His hand went to his beard to scratch it.

"Ha," he growled, "here is this beard of mine on my lazy head. You are not faithful, head. All day you sit on my shoulders and I have to carry you. You never do anything except gape at the world, and I have to feed you all the time. You ought to be ashamed of yourself for being so lazy. You are nothing but a rascal."

The sun was dropping down in the sky, and he got up to find a place for the night.

He walked and walked, grumbling against his lazy head and praising his walking legs, and so he came to a farm where smoke came from the chimney. He asked the master whether he could stay there for the night.

Yes he could, if he would clean the barn. The gypsy began shoveling. He didn't work too fast. But the master was a friendly soul and gave him a good meal and showed him a clean bed for the night.

The gypsy felt fine and sat around listening to the men talk and the dogs bark and then he went to his good bed.

He was still thinking of his faithful legs and his lazy head. He looked at the fine bed and said:

"That is a good place for you, faithful legs, to rest. You deserve a soft straw pillow. But you, you lazy head, you don't deserve anything. You should be beaten and punished, and I'm going to do it. I will teach you a lesson you'll remember. You'll sleep on the cold hard earth, not in a soft warm bed."

Then the Noodlehead gypsy put his legs on the good pillow and his head on the hard earth and fell asleep.

"You, faithful legs, deserve a soft pillow."

35. THE MAN, THE WOMAN, AND THE FLY

(Iceland)

There was once a household in Iceland where everyone was a Noodlehead except the flies. The flies were smart.

The man in the family churned a tub of butter for the winter. He put it in the cellar to keep it cool and covered it tight so no animal could get into it.

But the woman of the house loved butter, and now and then, when the husband was away working, she went down into the cellar, uncovered the butter, ate a good slab of it, and then covered it up again.

This she did again and again, and each time she ate bigger and bigger slabs of butter. Do you think she had any worries about what her husband would say, or that she was afraid? Not she! She was too silly to be scared or to worry. She just ate more and more of that butter, and there was less and less of it. Pretty soon there was not a speck of butter left.

Winter came, with snow and ice, and one day the man said:

"Wife, we have a nice tub of butter in the cellar. Go down and bring up some so we can eat it with our bread."

"I'll bring up some butter, good husband." And she really meant it—for she was so silly she had fogotten about eating it all up. Or maybe she hadn't!

She went down and soon came back, dragging the tub after her. The husband took the cover off and saw —it was empty!

"Wife, where is all the butter? What has happened to it? Do you know where it is, wife?" He looked at the tub, eyes and mouth open. So did the silly wife. She put her head deep into the tub to look better.

The room was warm from the stove, and a big, fat fly had gotten way down in that butter tub.

When the woman's head went in, the fly zoomed up and she saw it.

"Ah, husband," the woman cried, "there is the thief! Do you see that fat, black fly inside the tub? She ate all the butter, I'm sure."

"I always knew you were smart, wife. No thief can

escape you. Wait and don't make any noise. I'll show you what I'll do to that thief!" the husband said. He ran to the next room and found a big hammer with which he pounded his dry fish.

"I'll pound you to pieces, you thief!" he mumbled in his beard. "Now, wife, close the door so that thief can't fly off."

She closed the door quickly, while the fly began zooming around the room and the man began chasing it.

Wherever the fly stopped, bang! went the hammer, but only the furniture was hurt—the fly was off. Chairs went down, so did tables and dishes. The fly kept on flying, the man kept on chasing, and the hammer kept on breaking. In the end, the old man was tired from running and hammering, beating and breaking.

He sat down, breathing hard. The fly was still zooming around and around and then landed on the sitting man's nose.

"Here's your chance to get that fly, wife," he said. "Quick, kill it!"

The woman picked up the nearest stick and began hitting the man on the nose. The fly flew away and the man's nose was broken, and that is the end of the story.

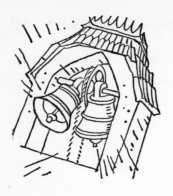

36. FOOLS' BELLS RING IN EVERY TOWN

(Italy)

"Silly folks are in my home and silly folks are in my village," said young Pietro. "I'll try to find a place where there are no silly folks." He took bread and cheese and wine and made a bundle and set off, looking to find Paradise.

At night he came to a village and entered a farmhouse where a light was burning.

"Have you room for the night for a tired fellow?" he asked.

"We have plenty of room, stranger," said the young couple sitting at the table at their evening meal. "Sit down with us and have bread and meat."

He sat down and they ate and they talked and soon

he saw that the brains in their heads would not cast long shadows. In other words, they were far from smart.

After supper, they went to sleep, and with the cock's crow they arose. Pietro was near dressed and he heard the young wife in the kitchen getting breakfast and from the next room he heard a thumping and a jumping.

"Who can be jumping in that room so early in the morning?" He went to see. There was a strange sight indeed. On the floor lay a pair of gray woolen stockings, the tops stretched apart; and there was the young husband, jumping at them all the time.

"What are you trying to do, friend?"

"I am in trouble, stranger. My wife knitted me this fine pair of stockings for my birthday, which is today, and I want to put them on. I have been trying to jump into them for nearly half an hour and I have no luck. My feet just won't get inside."

Pietro looked at him for some time. Then he looked at the stockings on the floor, and then he said:

"Friend, you fed me and gave me a good bed to sleep in. For this I will teach you a way to put stockings on your feet without jumping into them."

"I will thank you for that, for I want my wife to see how nice the stockings look on me," said the husband.

"Well, friend, sit down on the edge of the bed and do as I tell you." He picked up a stocking, spread the top apart, and pulled it on the fellow's foot. He did the same for the other foot.

"Thanks to the Saints for sending you here, good stranger," the host cried, beaming. "You have helped me in my trouble. I thank you."

"You don't have to thank me. I am glad to repay you for your hospitality."

Pietro ate a good breakfast and then went off. "This village is no better than mine. It has its own silly folks just the same as mine," he thought.

He walked along the dusty road and came to a village in the hills. Maybe it was Montieri,* in which, the people of Siena say, are the most foolish people in all of Italy.

He entered an inn and sat down to eat. Soon twelve men came in with long faces.

"Host," said Pietro, "you have many guests tonight."

"These are not guests. They are the night-watchers-for-the-sunrise."

"What are night-watchers-for-the-sunrise?"

"They watch, one for each hour, during the night for the sun to rise, and the one who sees the sun first over the mountains rings a bell to rouse the whole vil-

* See *The Priceless Cats and Other Italian Folk Stories*, by M. A. Jagendorf. Published by The Vanguard Press, New York, N. Y.

lage. Otherwise we would not know when to get up and would sleep through the whole day."

Pietro looked and thought: In this village folly grows stronger than weeds. Then he said, "Is this the best way you can tell when the sun rises?"

"We know no other," said the innkeeper, "and we are very unhappy about it. None of us likes to lose an hour's sleep. Worse luck is that it tells us that we must go to work. We don't like it at all, but what can we do? It is better to have one stay up an hour at a time than have the whole village sitting up the night long to see when the sun rises. We have done it for many years."

"Good friend," said Pietro, "what will you give me if I show how you can tell when the sun rises, without a single person losing a single hour's sleep?"

"We will pay you a good sum," said the innkeeper and the twelve village men who were listening to the conversation. "An hour's sleep is worth money."

"Friends," cried Pietro, "this is the last night you lose your hour's sleep, I promise you." They agreed on the price, and then all the men toasted Pietro again and again for the good news. Then everybody except the first watch for the night went to sleep.

The next morning Pietro and everyone else got up when they heard the ringing of the bell that told of the rising of the sun. They ate a good breakfast and with good wishes and cheers from the village, Pietro went off, promising to return.

He walked until he came to a village where he found a strong, big, red-feathered rooster and brought it back to the town to the "night-watchers-for-the-sunrise." Everyone crowded around Pietro.

"What kind of bird is that?" they cried. They had never seen a rooster.

"It's a sun bird."

"What is a sun bird?"

"It is a bird that tells when the sun rises. He will ring a special kind of bell that he carries with him in his throat. It doesn't go *ting-a-ling-a-ling,* but it goes *kikeriki, kikeriki.* When you hear that, you can get up, for then you will know the sun has risen."

"Are you sure of that?"

"Let us try the sun bird this very night," Pietro said.

There was great excitement in the town through the day and night. Many villagers sat up through the dark hours to see if the sun bird would really tell when the sun would rise with his *kikeriki* ringing.

Then . . . suddenly there was a loud *kikeriki!* The sun peeped over the mountains! The sun bird stood on a dung heap crowing *kikeriki* again and again.

The sun bird stood crowing kikeriki.

The villagers cheered until they were hoarse. Pietro got the money they had promised, and he went off, his head high and a smile on his face.

"This village is no better than mine," Pietro said. "It has its own silly folk, the same as mine."

He came to the next village and knocked at a house where a light shone. A young farmer, with a face as long as a long day, opened the door.

"Good evening, friend."

"Come in," said the farmer without a smile. Pietro entered and sat down.

"Why do you look so sad?" Pietro asked.

"I have a difficult problem."

"What is your problem?"

"I bought this farm a year ago and grew a fine crop of walnuts on it. They are there in the corner in a big heap and here are the two sacks in which I want to put them to take to the market to sell. All day long I have tried to put them into the sacks with that fork and I can't. They just won't stay on the fork."

"Show me how you did it."

"I will." The poor simple silly went to the table, picked up an iron fork in one hand and a bag in the other, and went to the heap of walnuts. There he tried to stick the prongs of the fork into the walnuts. Of course they wouldn't go into the hard shell.

Pietro watched him for a time and then he said:

"Good friend, there is another way to put the walnuts into the bag that you can do very easily."

"Show me and I will give you a share of the nuts," the young farmer said eagerly.

"That I will, gladly," said Pietro. "Look!" And he picked up two handfuls of nuts and threw them into the sack. He did that a few times.

"See," said he, "how easy it is." The young fellow watched him, a big smile on his face.

"That's fine. Why didn't I think of it? Now I will take the walnuts to the market and sell them and earn a good copper. Come, let us eat and drink. You deserve a fine meal for this."

They ate and they drank deep into the night.

The next morning the farmer went to the market with two bags of walnuts, and Pietro went off with a bag of walnuts for himself, but he didn't go to market with the farmer. He went back along the same road by which he had come.

"I've had enough traveling," he cried. "Folks are the same all over."

So he went home.

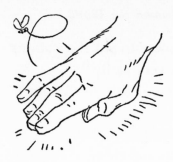

37. GIUFÁ AND THE JUDGE

(Italy)

Every country in the world has someone famous for the silly things he does and for the silly way in which he behaves. In Italy it was Giufá who always was doing things that made people laugh.

One summer the flies gave him no peace. He'd flap his hands and stamp his feet, but it helped little.

"I'll teach you flies how to behave," and to the judge he went to complain.

"What do you want in court?" the judge, who knew Giufá, asked.

"I am here to complain."

"To complain against what? What has been done to you?"

"I am here to complain against the flies."

"Against the flies!" the judge cried.

"Yes, against the flies in my house."

"What crime have they committed?"

"They give me no peace. They bite and sting, and I never did any harm to them."

The judge laughed and said, "Giufá, I am afraid I can't do anything about that."

"You are the judge, and it is you who must punish those who do wrong. I leave the flies in peace, but they don't leave me in peace. They are forever stinging me and biting. They should be punished for that."

The judge laughed again, and so did the whole court.

"Giufá, I can't punish the flies, but I give you permission to kill any fly wherever you see it."

It so happened that a fly, which had been buzzing in the judge's chamber, settled on the judge's nose at that very minute.

Without saying a word, Giufá made a fist and aimed a fine blow right at the judge's nose.

It killed the fly, but it hurt the judge and nearly broke his nose. But what could the judge say? He just made a face and cried, "Don't you ever come into my chambers again."

38. DONKEY AND SCHOLARS

(Flemish)

Uphill and downhill, Tyll,* the merry jester, wandered while King Summer reigned in the land. Each day it was uphill and downhill, through green valleys and yellow fields, and between trees hung with ripe fruits. Tyll sang with joy all the time. When he went up a hill he sang gaily because he was thinking how easy it would be going down the other side; and each time he walked down a hill he was merry because he thought how pleasant it would be to go through the valley.

So he came to the city of Erfurt, where there is a

---

* For other tales of Tyll, see *Tyll Ulenspiegel's Merry Pranks* by M. A. Jagendorf. Published by The Vanguard Press, New York, N. Y.

university full of professors and students. Tyll decided to find out how wise they were.

He posted on the doors of the Erfurt University notices that he, too, could teach any creature, however stupid, to read and write.

The scholars and doctors of Erfurt had heard of Tyll's cleverness in arguments and answers, so they put their heads together for a long time to think of a way to get the better of him. For not only did they want to teach Tyll a lesson, but to prove to the world that they were the smartest scholars in the world. They discussed and argued from the early morning hours until late in the night and finally the greatest scholar spoke:

"That vagabonding lout says he can teach any creature to read and write. Now, 'creature' means dumb beast as well as human being. Why not bring him some beast to try his skill? That will be better than arguing with him. Therefore let us bring him the animal that is most famous for its stupidity—by this I mean the donkey—and demand that he teach a donkey to read and write. If he fails, as he must, we shall drive him in shame from our city and announce to all the world that we got the better of him whom no one has ever bested. This will make us the most famous university not only in all Germany but in all the world."

All the learned gentlemen decided that it was a fine

idea, and they called Tyll to come before the rector. When he answered the summons, Tyll was told he would have to prove his statement by teaching an ass of Erfurt to read and write. For he had said he could teach any creature, and "creature" meant animal, too.

Tyll heard this and was well pleased.

"I will do as you bid me, learned master; all I ask is enough time in which to do my work."

Nothing could be said against that, and so they agreed upon five years.

"Now you must provide me with the pupil, the school, and board and lodging. For now I am a professor, if only to teach a donkey."

That was fair enough, and the rector said:

"There are many donkeys in Erfurt, and we shall send you one of them. Stay with him at the inn, and we shall give you enough to live on."

When Tyll was alone in the inn with his donkey, he spoke to him and said:

"Friend Long Ears, I want you to know that I have struck a fine bargain. There are three of us in this affair—you, I, and the rector. Five years is a long time. If the rector, who is an old man, dies, I am free of the contract, for I made it with him. If you die, they must set me free of my obligation; if I die, there'll be no one to keep the contract. Of these three things, one must happen in so many years. In the meanwhile, friend, we shall live in great ease and happy comfort."

Thereafter, each and every day Tyll took an old psalter he had borrowed from the university into the manger and put it before the donkey. Between every two pages Tyll had placed some oats. The donkey, scenting the food, would push the leaves back and forth with his snout for the grains, and, when he had eaten them all and could find no more, he would keep on with his search, braying all the time: *Eeee, Eeee-a, Eeee-a, A-eeee.*

Soon the animal knew the trick well and would look for the oats whenever the psalter was put before him. Tyll went to the rector and said:

"Master rector, would you like to see how my pupil is getting along?"

"Has he gotten far?" asked the man of learning.

"As much as you would expect from a donkey. It has been difficult, but with hard work I finally have taught him part of the alphabet, particularly the vowels. Come to the inn and you will see for yourself."

The rector said he would come the next day, after his noon meal.

Tyll did not give the donkey any food that day, and when the rector and a large number of university masters came, the beast showed great restlessness.

"My pupil is much excited and would like to show

you what a fine pupil he is, as is the way of new students," said Tyll, placing the book before the donkey.

No sooner did the animal see it than he began to push the leaves in all directions in search of the oats. Not finding any, he began to bray aloud: *Eeee, Eeee-a, Eeee-a, A-eeee.*

"Masters," said Tyll, "the ass already knows two vowels: 'A' and 'E.' He reads them aloud when he sees them in the psalter. Observe how he turns the pages, looking for them all the time. With the aid of the Lord, and my hard labor, he will soon read as well as any learned scholar in Erfurt, or, for that matter, in Germany."

The rector and the scholars went away in great astonishment.

Tyll lived in plenty and pleasure until the spring, when the rector passed on to the better world. This left Tyll free, and he went from the city wondering why so many of the men of the universities are called scholars, when "Noodlehead" fitted them better.

39. SILLY MATT

(Norway)

Silly Matt of Norway! Who hasn't heard his name?
Everyone in Norway has, and now you will, too.

Silly Matt was forever making folks laugh with the
things he did. But his mother didn't like it too much—
for what mother likes to see her son do silly things all
the time?

"A wife will set you right. It's best for you to get
married," she said.

Matt had nothing against this. He thought he
would like a wife. So his mother sent him out to woo a
wife.

"Go, son," she said. "If you find a good one, you may
bless your stars and cry 'Hurrah!'"

Matt went off and came to Solvy's farm. Solvy was

pretty, Solvy had pink cheeks and blue eyes, Solvy was always laughing. Matt wooed her in his silly way, but Solvy was kind and thought he wasn't such a bad fellow. If he couldn't do anything else, he could make her laugh with his silly ways, and Solvy loved to laugh.

She said, "Yes," she would have him.

Matt cried, "Hurrah!" and jumped up high and then ran to his mother to tell her the good news.

"It's fine, son, that you found a bride. You are lucky. What's your bride's name?"

Matt scratched his head, looked up and down and all around, and said he didn't know.

That made his mother angry. "Go right back and ask her name and come back here and tell it to me," she cried.

Matt ran to his bride's home. First he talked of this and then he talked of that and in the end he said:

"Please tell me your name."

She laughed and answered: "Well, you should know my name. It's Solvy."

Matt ran to tell his mother. He ran fast as a hare, but ofttimes running too fast only makes you late. As he ran, he kept on saying to himself:

> *"Solvy, Solvy,*
> *Is my darling.*

> *Solvy, Solvy,*
> *Is my darling."*

He ran through woods and through fields and then he came to a hillock. There he slipped on a tuft of grass and fell on his face. He hurt his nose so hard he saw stars before his eyes and forgot everything—even his bride's name. He got up and couldn't remember it.

"Lord! I lost my bride's name," he cried. "But I couldn't have lost it very far; it must be right on the hillock where I fell. It's somewhere in the grass. I must find it, or my mother will be angry."

He began looking everywhere in the grass for his sweetheart's name, but with all his looking he could not find it anywhere.

Near him a spade lay in the grass. He began digging the ground with it. Perhaps his bride's name had slipped into the ground like a worm.

An old man came by. "What are you digging, Matt?" he asked. "Have you lost anything?"

"That I have, indeed. I lost my bride's name. She just gave it to me, and I lost it when I fell on the grass right here."

The old man knew Matt. He also knew that Matt was wooing Solvy.

"Solvy is your bride's name, and it is a great wonder she will marry you."

"Oh yes, that's her name," Matt cried joyfully. "That's her name. Thank you, sir," and again he ran off, crying:

> *"Solvy, Solvy,*
> *Is my darling.*
>
> *Solvy, Solvy,*
> *Is my darling."*

He had run a short way when he felt the spade that didn't belong to him still in his hands. He rushed back toward the hillock and threw it down with all his might. It fell right on the feet of the old man who was resting there. The old man began to cry, and when Matt heard him cry he felt so bad that once again he forgot his bride's name. So he went home slowly.

"What is your bride's name?" his mother asked.

"I don't know, Mother," Matt said. "I had her name, she gave it to me, but I lost it twice. Once when I fell on the hillock, and once when the old man cried."

"Oh, Matt, you are the biggest fool in all Norway and I only hope your bride will make you a little wise. They say, to be better you must become worse, and you are the worst in the land."

"Mother, I promise I'll do better next time."

But the next time Matt did something else just as silly. Just as there is always some Matt doing something silly everywhere.

40. THE SCHILDA TOWN HALL

(Germany)

In Germany there was a town named Schilda, and the people there were the smartest people in all Germany. So emperors and princes ordered them to come to their courts to solve their problems, and the Schilda women had to stay at home to do the work. Since women are not strong and do not like to work in barns and fields, very little work got done. Soon the women wrote to the men to come home at once. The men came, and when they saw how home and hearth were neglected, they decided never to go away again!

But emperors and princes have power, and men must obey, so the Schilda men decided on a clever scheme so the rulers and nobles wouldn't bother them.

"It isn't so wonderful to be smart," they said. "Let us be foolish instead, and we will be left in peace."

Everyone agreed on this, and from that day on the men of Schilda began to act more foolish than fishes.

Now, you know when you do anything for a long time, you do it forever and can't do anything else. So in good time the Schilda citizens became the finest crop of Noodleheads in all Germany. From then on the emperors and princes never bothered them again.

One day the Schilda citizens decided to build a new town hall. They all set to work with bricks and mortar, and soon the finest town hall you ever saw stood there, built with three sides only. This, because three sides took less time to build than four sides. The roof was made of green-glazed tiles. Schilda men, women, and children stood around the building so happy they wanted to cry. Then everyone went inside, and all their joy died away. It was pitch black and cold. They banged into one another and knocked their heads against the walls. Everybody was unhappy. Then someone cried out in the dark:

"Bring burning pine branches, for we must have a town meeting this very minute."

Men ran out and came back with the burning pine torches, which made a lot of smoke but gave only a poor light.

There were ten thousand arguments and questions

as to why they did not have any light in their town hall, when every town hall in Germany had it. In the end, the oldest man in the village said:

"The simplest way is to carry sunshine into our town hall. It will give us warmth and light. Let us take bags and baskets and pots and pans to carry in the sunshine. Everyone must work—men, women, and children. This is a new idea and it will make us famous."

All the Schilda citizens agreed, and since it was the noon hour when the sun was strongest, they rushed home at once, to get their pots and pans and sacks and sieves and barrels and baskets. First they stood in the sun, holding pots and pans, sacks and sieves, high above their heads to catch the sun. Then they rushed back into the town hall, emptying the empty vessels. Some had brought shovels and tried shoveling in the sunshine. But though everyone worked hard, and sweat ran down their faces and backs, the town hall was still empty and black.

Just then a young man from a far country, his knapsack on his back, happened to pass through Schilda. He watched the townsfolk at their work with a puzzled face. Then he asked what they were doing. They explained their plight, and because he had traveled through the world they asked him for advice.

"Yes, I can help you, but it will cost money."

"We'll pay gladly," they cried, one and all. The young man slowly walked around the building, three times, looking at it up and down on all three sides. Then he pinched his nose and said slowly:

"All you need, good friends, is to take off the roof and you will have all the sun and warmth you want."

Everyone thought this was a fine idea and they paid him, and he went his way, whistling.

They began to work at once taking the roof off, and soon there was enough sunshine and warmth in the town hall to set hearts a-dancing. All summer long there was no rain in Schilda, and so the townspeople spent much time in their town hall discussing all the problems of the world.

Fall came, with its cold and rain, and they put the roof back on. Now it was dark and cold inside all over again. They sat on the benches shivering and shaking, with burning pine branches stuck in their caps so they could see one another. That didn't help much, for the room was full of smoke.

One day, the oldest Schilda citizen's pine torch dropped on the floor. He jumped up and down on it to put it out. The others rushed to help him, and their torches, which were stuck in their caps, fell down, too. The chamber was filled with heavy smoke and was blacker than pitch. They all groped around to find the way out, and one of them accidentally touched a crack in the wall through which came a light, as thin as a thread.

"Holy Jerusalem!" he cried. "Townsmen! Surely we are Noodleheads. Do you know why we have no light in our town hall? The crack in the wall reminded me. How could we be so forgetful? Friends, we forgot to put windows in our town hall!"

Everyone was shocked and surprised, and then and there in the dark it was decided to correct the fault at once. Windows were made, and from then on there was plenty of light in the town hall of Schilda.

41. THE STOVE AND THE TOWN HALL

(Germany)

The Schilda citizens were very happy in their lighted town hall, but winter winds were blowing, snow was flying thick, and it was cold inside. They carefully examined the rooms to find the fault. The three-sided town hall had been divided into three important chambers. First came the "talking chamber," where everyone discussed everything. Then there was a "joke chamber," where jokes were told so everyone could enjoy a good laugh. Then came the "sweat and bath chamber," where everyone could get fresh and clean for talking and laughing.

Day after day the citizens discussed the question of why it was cold in their town hall. One day the oldest citizen cried:

"I know the fault. We forgot to bring wood for heat. You know the proverb says 'Old fools are the best.'" And he laughed at his clever joke, and so did all the others.

They rushed out to get wood and soon returned, each with a stout log. But there was still something wrong. They had wood, yet it was still cold. Cold enough to freeze their breath. Suddenly they all shouted together:

"Ha! We forgot the stove."

Then the great question arose: Where to put the stove? Since there were only three rooms, one for talking, one for joking, and one for sweating, there was no place for a stove.

They turned the matter over many ways, but could not find an answer. Then up spoke the cowherd:

"We have plenty of room outside the town hall."

"But," said the butcher, "if the stove is outside, the wind and the snow will get the heat, and not we."

"We could put it close to the wall," answered the cowherd.

"I can help," said the baker. "I have a new rabbit's net and I could put it around the stove and so keep the heat from leaking out."

"That won't help," said the butcher.

"Here is the answer," cried the shoemaker. "Let us put the stove right next to the window so that we can see it. Let us use the baker's rabbit's net over the stove and let us thank the good baker for it. We can sit inside and watch the sizzling heat and we can open the window and let the heat in. Between seeing the nice, glowing heat and what will come in through the open window, we should have a nice warm winter inside our town hall."

Everyone thought this was a fine idea, and the plan was carried out. But alas! For that winter the good Schilda citizens sat freezing in their town house just the same. Looking at the fire did not make them warm, and the open window made it colder.

42. THE TAILOR FROM THE SEA

(Finland)

In the olden days in Finland there was a little village of Holmola, which was renowned from one end of the land to the other. All Finns knew of the people of Holmola because they were the silliest people in all Finland. They were real Noodleheads. Many, many tales are told of the silly things they did.

One day, a band of the men of Holmola were out fishing. They were walking along the strand with their catch when suddenly they saw a thick, long lobster.

They had never seen a lobster and stopped in great wonder to look at the creature. They tried to figure out what it was.

"It can't be a wolf," said one. "No, it can't be, it is flat on the ground."

"It is a strange beast from a far land," said an old Holmolite.

The lobster began crawling backward.

"Which are his legs and which are his hands?" cried another.

"It seems to me that he carries two scissors. Now, animals don't carry scissors, and therefore he can't be an animal," said another.

"Look at the threads he is dragging in the sand," cried another.

"I said he had shears on each side," cried the one who had said it, "and here are threads. Only tailors have shears and threads. Therefore he must be a tailor—a very young tailor. He is so small."

Everyone agreed on this, and they felt very happy about it because they did not like deep arguments.

"Let us take this strange tailor to the mayor. Maybe he wants to stay in our village," said one of the fishermen.

"It's a long walk and he is so little—I think we'd better carry him."

They pushed him into a basket and marched off to the mayor, and the mayor was much pleased.

"Our town needs another tailor. My own tailor was to come today to cut my new coat and he sent word that he had a cold. I'll try the new tailor. Come, wife, bring out the new cloth I bought."

The mayor's wife brought out the new cloth and spread it on the big table. Then they let the lobster out of the basket on the cloth. The lobster crawled back and forth over it, but the claws did not cut it.

"Ah," said the mayor, "he is not cutting it but showing us where we should cut it ourselves." So he took the big shears and began cutting wherever the lobster was crawling.

Soon all the cloth was cut in shreds. Cried the mayor's wife: "The cloth is cut in small pieces and it will never make a coat now. It's the new tailor's fault, and he should be punished for it."

"You are right, wife. He can't be a tailor in our town, and I'll make him pay dearly for my cloth," said the mayor in great anger. Then he turned to the lobster and cried, "Get out, you vagabond, you good-for-nothing!"

He got hold of the lobster to fling him off the table. This frightened the lobster, and he got hold of the mayor's hand, pinching it with all his might.

"Murder! Help!" the mayor roared. "He's trying to kill me with his shears. He is a traitor and a murderer! Help!"

They pulled at the lobster, flinging him into the basket, but the mayor kept on shouting:

"This villain sneaked into our peaceful town to cheat us and murder us. We must punish him. We'll try him right here."

So the lobster was tried and condemned to death.

Then the question arose: What kind of death was it to be for so terrible a crime? Hanging would be too long, and cutting off the head too short. Besides, no one was sure where the head was.

"He was found by the sea—let him drown in the sea. Drowning in water is the worst kind of death," said the mayor.

So they took the lobster to the sea, and the bailiff rowed him far out.

"Now, the punishment," the mayor cried.

And the bailiff flung the basket out into the water.

The lobster got out and began swimming around, rocking from side to side.

"Look how he suffers," cried the Finns standing on the shore. "But he is getting what he deserves."

Then the lobster disappeared into the deep sea, and the Holmolites went home, satisfied that justice had been done.

43. AILI'S QUILT

(Finland)

In far Finland where the snow is thick and winds blow wild, the winters are very long and very cold. So folks have good fires to keep them warm in the bright daylight and thick coverings to keep them warm in the dark nights. Men are always bringing wood from the forests and women are forever making quilts of wool. The nicest present a Finnish wife can give her husband for his birthday is a nice new woolen quilt or a patch quilt.

And this was true of Holmola, as of every other town in that far country.

Now, there lived in that famous town, where folks are blessed with little brains and big kindness, a good man and his good wife in their little *kotta*—that is, a house of bark built like an Indian wigwam.

The good wife, whose name was Aili, was making a fine patch quilt for her husband Kalle (which is the Finnish name for Charles). She made it of pieces of cloth and wool of every color—like Joseph's coat in the Bible—and she was very proud of it. When it was finished, she called in all her neighbors to see it, and everyone agreed it was beautiful. And Kalle thought it was the most beautiful quilt in all Finland.

"Aili, my dear wife," he said, "Aili, you are a good wife. I was lucky to marry one who is so clever and can make such a wonderful quilt. It is beautiful!"

Then they ate their night meal and went to sleep, and Kalle covered himself with the new quilt.

It was a cold night, and Kalle pulled the quilt over his ears. But when he did, his feet were out in the cold —the quilt was too short. Even when he pulled up his knees, his feet still stuck out. But Finns can stand a lot of cold, and he slept through the night.

In the morning Kalle said:

"Aili, the beautiful quilt you made for me is too short. Each time I pull it over my ears, it does not cover my feet, and my feet get cold."

"I will fix that," said Aili. She thought for a time, then she said: "Good husband, did you say the quilt covered your ears but not your feet?"

"That's right, Aili. My neck and ears and face were covered and warm, but my feet were not and were cold. It's too short at the feet."

"Oh, I can fix that," cried Aili. "After breakfast I will get to work so you can use it tonight. You just show me which end covered your neck and ears."

Kalle showed her the end, and after breakfast she took her shears and cut off a good wide piece from that end. This she sewed to the other end.

"Now," she said, "this will take care of dear Kalle's feet."

At night they went to sleep and Kalle again used the new quilt. But after he covered his neck and ears and face, his feet once more were out in the cold, just as they had been the night before. The next morning he told this to Aili.

"Perhaps I did not cut off enough at the neck," she said.

So once more she cut off a wide piece at the end that covered Kalle's neck and sewed it to the opposite end.

Now, you who do not live in Holmola know that that did not make the quilt any longer. But the two sillies of Holmola did *not* know that. As the Finnish proverb goes: You need sense for work and music for dancing.

But after his neck was covered, his feet were once more out in the cold, just as they had been the night before.

Aili kept on cutting at one end and sewing to the other until she grew tired and decided it was best to make a new quilt. And Kalle and Aili hoped the new one would be long enough. And so do you and I.

44. KULTANI, THE NOODLE GOSSIP

(Finland)

Once there lived in Finland a husband and a wife. The husband's name was Matti, and the wife's name was Kultani. She was a very silly woman, just like the women of Holmola—no, she was worse. Not only was she very silly, but she was the worst gossip in all Finland and spoke more words than there are fish in the sea.

Whatever she heard, whether it made sense or not, she would burn to tell it to all the village before you could count three.

You can imagine what kind of life Matti had.

One day he was out examining his fish nets in the

lake and his snares in the woods when he stumbled into a hole and hit something hard. He dug away the earth, and there was a horde of gold. Much gold—so much that it was too much for him to carry home alone. But to ask his wife's help would spread the news all over the village, and that he did not want. So he covered the treasure and went home slowly. You know, time always brings wisdom.

That day he had caught in his fish net a big pike and in a snare a heavy woodcock. He was thinking about how to stop his silly wife from telling all Finland of his treasure when he had an idea. He ran to the net and took out the pike and went to the snare and took out the woodcock. Then he put the fish into the bird snare. The woodcock he took to the lake and put in the net. Then he went home.

When he reached his house he said, "Wife, the Lord has blessed us. I found a great treasure in the woods today. Tomorrow we will go and bring it home."

"What! You found a treasure in the woods?" Kultani cried, jumping up and down. She was burning to rush out and tell it to all the neighbors. "I must run out and tell everyone the good news."

"No," Matti said, "don't tell it to anyone. If you do, they will take it away from us. It is late and I am hungry. Let us eat and go to bed. Tomorrow we will bring the treasure home." And he would not let her leave the house.

The next morning, early, the two set out for the woods, each carrying a stout basket. They walked until they came to the lake.

"Oh," Matti said, "I caught something in the net. I was so excited about the treasure that I forgot to bring it home. Come, let us get it."

They went to the net and there was the woodcock.

"A woodcock in a fish net! There never was anything like it in all Finland!" Kultani screamed. "I must run back to the village and tell everybody."

"You can't," said Matti. "Now we are going to get the treasure."

They took the woodcock and walked on. Soon they came near the snare.

"Oh," said Matti, "I caught something yesterday in one of the snares, but I was too excited to bring it home. Come, let us get it."

They came to the pike in the snare.

"A pike in a snare in the woods!" Kultani screamed. "That never happened in Finland before. I must run to the village and tell everyone!"

"No, you don't," said Matti. "Now we are going for the treasure."

They took the pike and walked to the place where the gold was, filled their baskets, and turned back.

No sooner did they reach the village than Kultani wanted to tell the news to everybody, but Matti held her tight by the skirt. As they walked along, she was burning more and more to talk. In the end, she tore herself away. At the time, they were right before a *tupa* (a house) from which there came a howling and yowling of dogs. Kultani was running right to it.

"Don't go there," cried Matti. "Don't you hear the wife beating her husband? If you go in, maybe you'll be beaten, too. Don't you hear him howling like a dog?"

Kultani was frightened and walked close to Matti until they got home.

"I am terribly hungry," said Matti, to keep Kultani from running out. "Give me something to eat."

While she was busy in the kitchen, Matti hid the gold. It was late by then, and they went to sleep.

Early the next morning Kultani couldn't stand it any more. She dashed out of the house while Matti was cutting wood and raced into the house where Matti had said the wife was beating her husband.

"What do you think!" she screamed. "Matti found a treasure! Lots of gold!"

People heard her screaming and came to see and hear.

"Matti found a treasure! Baskets full of gold! And he caught a woodcock in the lake in his net and a pike in the snare in the woods! It's truly a marvel!"

"Are you out of your mind?" folks said. "You were always known as a Noodlehead, but this is the worst we ever heard. Whoever heard of a pike caught in a snare in the woods and a woodcock caught in the lake? Only fools believe such tales. You are a true Holmolite, where fools are born and bred."

"Believe me, I tell the truth," she screamed. "We brought home two baskets of gold, which my husband hid I don't know where. I saw the fish in the snare in the woods and the woodcock in the net in the lake. I wanted to tell it to you last night when I passed here, but your wife was beating you. I heard you howling so I did not come in."

"What! My wife was beating me?" roared the good man. "You heard me howling? You are crazy! My wife never touched me, and I never opened my mouth. You are either crazy or the most stupid woman in all the world, or both. Get out of my house. I never want to see your face again. Your husband found a treasure like he found a woodcock in a fish net. Out of my house! You are a troublemaker, like all fools and gossips."

He got hold of her by the ear and put her out.

From that day on everyone laughed at whatever Kultani said and did not believe it, so she stopped gossiping and talking, and that is the end of my story.

45. THE OBEDIENT SERVANT

(Hungary)

Somewhere in the land of Hungary, I don't know where, there was a silly fellow. He was walking along the road and saw a wagon.

"Where there is a wagon there must be horses, and where there are horses, my heart belongs. I'll hire myself out as driver," he thought.

He went to the master of the farm. "Do you need a driver?" he asked.

"Do you know horses and wagons?" the master asked.

"As much as a Hungarian knows about *paprika*."*

* Paprika is a yellow-red spice Hungarian people use a great deal in their cooking. I have known Hungarians to pronounce it papri-kash.

"You know enough and you are hired. Tomorrow we go to town. Harness four horses to the wagon early in the morning. Two before and two behind. You understand?"

"That I do."

The next morning Noodlehead rose early, harnessed two horses, and hitched them to the front of the wagon. The other two he harnessed and tied to the back of the wagon.

The master came out.

"Idiot!" he roared. "What did you do? I told you to harness the four horses, two before the others. Don't you understand, thick-skull? The four horses go in front, two behind the others."

"Forgive me, master. Next time I'll do better." He took the two he had tied to the back and hitched them in front of the other horses, talking all the time and telling how he would do better next time.

But the master was still angry. Said he grimly: "You fool, stop blabbering. Sit in back; I'll drive in front— only keep quiet. Keep your silly mouth shut."

They drove along the *Puszta,* that is, along the plain, while white storks flew overhead. Soon the spikes holding the back wheels of the wagon dropped out and the wheels started to come loose. Noodlehead saw this, but remembering what he had been told, he kept his mouth tight shut.

"Numskull! Dolt! Didn't you see the wheels sliding off?"

The back wheels were sliding off. Still Noodlehead kept his mouth tight shut. The wheels fell off; the wagon went down with a crash; the horses stopped short. The master turned around and saw the sight.

"Idiot! Numskull! Dolt! Didn't you see the wheels sliding off?" he roared.

"That I did, master."

"Why didn't you tell me?"

"You told me to keep my mouth tight shut and I couldn't talk with my mouth tight shut."

"Great sixes and sevens! Is there a greater numskull in all Magyar-land than you?"

"I don't know."

"Get out of my sight," bellowed the master, "and run to Buda [that is, Budapest, the capital of Hungary] on your stupid legs."

Noodlehead jumped out of the wagon and began running toward Budapest as he was told.

The city was hundreds of miles away.

46. THE HERO

(Hungary)

When it was good, it wasn't bad, and when it was bad, it wasn't good.

Noodlehead was running on the road to Budapest, the capital of Hungary. Soon he grew tired and sat down. Along came a blind man feeling his way with a stick.

"God bless you, father," said Noodlehead.

"And God bless you, son. From your voice I take you to be a young fellow."

"I am a young fellow and I've just lost my master. He told me to run to Buda. I ran until I got tired."

"Buda is far away. Why don't you come with me

212

and be my eyes? Life will be simple for you, for folks always help me. You'll have food and lodging."

They made a pact, and soon both were on the high road with the wind behind them. The sun was moving in the heaven.

"What do you see, son?" the blind man asked.

"A monastery, father."

"That's lucky. When you see the monks, we'll beg for alms and then we will get food and lodging for the night."

"What do monks look like, father?"

"They are all in black."

A herd of black cattle came on the road. Cried Noodlehead: "The monks are coming! A whole herd of them."

The blind man ran right into the herd begging for alms. The animals became frightened, began to bellow, knocked them both down, and ran off.

"A curse on you, you fool!" cried the blind man. "Away from me, for you will only bring me misfortune."

So Noodlehead picked himself up and went his way.

"I'd better go home," he said. "There I am scolded, too, but I also get something to eat and a place to sleep." So he turned homeward. Night came, and he saw light in the distance. He came to the light and saw seven men with evil faces eating and drinking.

"Would you give me a little food and let me stay here for the night?" he asked.

"First tell us who you are, what you do, and where you are going."

He told them his name, and of his last adventures. They saw he belonged to the tribe that believes the moon runs around the sky with bare feet.

They gave him food and told him he could stay at the fire while they went away on business.

"There are wild animals around here, so you'd better sleep in that empty barrel that is open at one end. There you'll be safe," one of the men said.

Noodlehead crept into the barrel, and the men went off. It wasn't long before a giant wolf with long fangs came sniffing and smelling. Noodlehead was wide awake. The wolf got at the bones the men had left behind.

Those bones lay near the barrel, and the wolf was crunching them, his back to the barrel. After a time his tail got into the opening and it was swishing into Noodlehead's face and tickling him.

That's the size of a good-sized pony. Maybe it'll pull me home, Noodlehead thought.

So he got hold of the wolf's long tail and wound it tight around his arm.

The wolf, not knowing what held his tail, became frightened and began to run, pulling the barrel after him.

Heigh ho! They flew along over hill and dale until they came right into Noodlehead's village, where folks were sitting around smoking their pipes and gossiping.

When the villagers saw a wild wolf dragging a new kind of carriage, they thought it came from a better world.

Noodlehead let go the wolf's tail. The wolf ran away and Noodlehead came out of the barrel.

"Good day, father," he said. "It's hard to lose a broken hoof."

For once no one called him Noodlehead, for anyone who came riding into the village on the tail of a wolf wasn't just a Noodlehead, he was a *hero*.

47. LUCK FOR FOOLS

(Austria)

Hansl married Liesl, and there weren't two more foolish peasants in the Tyrol in Austria.

One day Hansl took his cow to sell. It was a long walk to the market, and the cow walked slowly. Sometimes she stopped to chew grass. Wherever there was a puddle, she splashed mud on Hansl with her hoofs. It was slow going, and Hansl grumbled and growled.

"It's a long way to the market," he said. He was getting angry enough to make geese laugh.

A peasant in short green leather pants and a feather

in his hat came from the opposite direction, driving a goat to the market to sell.

"Good day, good friend," said the goat man. "You look like the sun forgot to shine."

"I am angry because that stupid cow of mine, which I am taking to the market to sell, is dragging along like a snail."

"You'll get there in good time. I am going to the market to sell my goat. We'll meet there."

"Ha," thought Hansl, "perhaps I can get rid of this slow beast."

"Tell you what, friend," Hansl said aloud, "give me your goat for my cow. That'll save me the long walk to market, and your business will be finished, too."

The goat farmer opened his eyes wide. A cow for a goat! There's no end to fools' deeds in this world, he was thinking.

"Fine, fine," he cried. "I'll take your slow-poke cow from you and give you my lively goat for it, and may the Lord bless you and keep you as you are."

They changed animals, and Hansl went homeward, cheerfully whistling and thanking his good luck for having gotten rid of the silly cow for a fine, lively goat.

But alas! The goat was too lively. It kept on meckering without end. It pulled the rope this way and that way until Hansl's hands ached. It ran and pulled him along; it stopped and wouldn't go. Hansl's legs began to ache, too, from running.

Then suddenly the goat turned on him and began butting him with its horns. It seemed to like the game and kept it up. Poor Hansl was at his wits' end. He was getting angrier by the minute and tried to think how he could get rid of that wild beast.

A peasant woman came up the road driving a herd of geese.

" 'Morning, good woman. Would you like to change my goat for a goose?"

"Your goat for *one* of my geese?" she cried. The woman couldn't believe her ears. A goat was worth ten geese.

"Aye, my goat for one of your geese. My wife wants a goose badly."

"You're sure you want to make this barter?" she asked.

"On my word."

The woman took a goose and gave it to Hansl and then ran off quickly to make sure he wouldn't change his mind.

Hansl put his rope around the goose's neck and walked off, happy with his bargain.

But joy does not last forever, even with fools. The goose hopped around worse than the goat. It flew all over, and Hansl had to chase it till he was out of breath.

"Unlucky man that I am!" he cried aloud. "This goose is the worst of all. I'd sell it for a bag full of old cow manure."

A peasant girl, standing at the gate, heard that. Quickly she ran to the yard, filled a bag full of dry cow manure, and ran after Hansl.

"Here is a bag full of cow manure for your goose."

"I said I'd sell it for that, and here it is. Old cow manure is fine fertilizer for a garden."

Hansl was happy and marched along, the cow manure under his arm. Soon he came to an inn. He sat down at a table and ordered a good supper. Two noblemen had come in and sat down not far from him. It didn't take long before they saw the bag of manure on the chair.

"Where did you get it, and why do you carry it around with you?" one asked.

Hansl told the noblemen his adventures, beginning with the cow.

"And now I am on my way home to tell my wife of the day's business."

The two noblemen saw quickly they were listening to one who believed that feathers grow on snails' houses.

"When you get home, your wife will give you black

words, and maybe she'll have the stick dancing a polka on your back," one said laughingly.

"My wife will be glad to see me and will give me good words of greeting," Hansl said.

"Not if I know women."

"You don't know my wife."

"I'm willing to bet she's no different from other wives."

"I will bet anything you want," Hansl said angrily.

"Well, Hansl," the nobleman said, "I'll bet you a hundred thalers you'll get a drubbing and a scolding."

"My wife will be sweet as honey when I come home, and I take your bet."

So the three left for Hansl's home, which was not far away.

When they arrived, there was Liesl at the door.

"Where have you been, Hansl dear?" she cried. "I worried about you. Did you sell the cow at a good price?"

"I changed it for a goat."

"That's good, the meadow was never enough for that big cow, but there'll be just enough for the goat. Where is it?"

"I changed the goat for a goose."

"Here's where he gets it," one nobleman said to the other.

"You did just the right thing, Hansl. Two of our pillow cases are empty, and now we'll have fine goose feathers for them. Where is the goose?"

"I changed it for a bag of dung."

"You are the smartest husband in all the Tyrol. Now how did you guess it? Today I went to our neighbor to borrow a little salt. And what do you think she said to me, Hansl?"

"What, Liesl?"

"She said, 'Liesl, you'd come borrowing if you needed a bit of manure.' Now we have our own manure and I don't have to go borrowing to our neighbors for anything. You brought home just the right thing. Hansl, you did a fine day's business."

What could the nobles say? Nothing! They just paid the hundred thalers and went their way saying: "There's no luck like fools' luck."

48. TANDALA AND PAKALA

(Rumania)

Have you heard of Tandala and Pakala? Maybe you haven't, but every man, woman, and child in Rumania has. Just say these two names to anyone from Bucharest to Sucava and there'll be good laughs. No wonder, for these two did more things to make folks laugh than all the people of Rumania put together.

Many tales are told about them, but the way these two came together is as good as any written with golden letters on yellow parchment.

Tandala was a very silly Noodlehead. If you'd hang a bell around his neck, he'd think he was inside a church. But Pakala was different. He was the worst rogue in Rumania. He was always up to any trick that would bring him gain or fame.

One day Tandala noticed a heap of old turnip leaves that had been in the fields for weeks and had turned grayish white.

"What a fine heap of wool," said Tandala. "I'll take it to the market and sell it at a good price." He stuffed it into a sack, tied a bell around his wrist so he wouldn't get lost, and set off for the market.

On the same day Pakala was finishing the last nut he had in his cupboard. He loved to eat nuts, and now he had nothing but nutshells.

"Oh," he sighed, "nuts are good to eat and I have only hard shells left. I'll take them to market—perhaps I'll find some fool who'll buy them."

He put all the broken nutshells in a sack, tied it, put it on his back, and went off whistling.

Not far from the town the Noodlehead Tandala and the rogue Pakala met.

"Good morning, brother," said Pakala, "why do you walk with a bell around your wrist?"

"Good morning to you, friend. I wear a bell around my wrist to make sure I won't get lost."

"Ah!" said Pakala, "I see." He knew at once that here was a fellow whose head was like one of the empty shells in his sack. "And where are you going, friend?" he asked again.

"I'm going to market to sell the bag of wool I am carrying on my shoulders. And where are you going with your sack on your back, brother?"

"I, too, am going to market—to sell a bag of fine nuts."

"Ah! Nuts are fine eating. I like nuts," said Tandala.

"Good friend," said Pakala, "I need a bag of wool and you like nuts. Why drag ourselves all the way to the market with these heavy bags on our shoulders when we can do business right here? Let's save the soles of our sandals. I'll give you my bag of nuts for your bag of wool. That will be a fair exchange."

"It will be fair, indeed," said Tandala. "I will gladly do it."

So Tandala the Noodlehead gave to Pakala the rogue his useless bag of old turnip tops, while Pakala the rogue gave his useless bag of nutshells to Tandala the Noodlehead. Then each turned back on the homeward road, satisfied with his bargain.

The sun was getting hotter, and soon each was tired and sat down to rest and to open the bag and see the bargain he had made.

Tandala opened the bag and saw the empty nutshells.

"Lord!" he cried. "Some witch ate the nuts off my back and left the empty shells. I must find the nut merchant and tell him that." So he turned back on the road.

Pakala opened his bag and saw the worthless turnip leaves.

"Did that fellow play a trick on me or is he a dumbhead who took these old leaves for wool? I must go back and find out." So he turned back on the road.

Soon the two met at the very same place the bargain had been struck.

"Hail, friend," cried Tandala from afar. "Some witch ate the nuts while I was walking and left me nothing but shells. Did you ever hear of such a thing?"

"Indeed I have," said Pakala. "A sister to that witch turned the wool you sold me into old turnip leaves. That's all there is in the sack."

"No!"

"Yes. Witches followed both of us and," said Pakala, "I think if we two stick to each other I am sure we can beat them. Why don't you and I travel together from now on? I am sure luck will follow our footsteps."

"If you think so, I agree," said Tandala. "Maybe the Saints brought us together. What happened to the wool in your sack and the nuts in mine is a sure sign."

"That's gospel," said Pakala. "From now on, you and I are blood brothers traveling through the world and sharing all that comes our way."

"Fine! What is your name, brother?"

"They call me Pakala, the rogue. And what is your name?"

"They call me Tandala, the fool."

So the rogue and the fool set off through the length and breadth of Rumania, and many funny things happened to them, as funny as when the Noodlehead fooled the rogue and the rogue fooled the Noodlehead.

"A sister to that witch turned the wool you sold me into old turnip leaves."

49. BELMONT ANTICS

(Switzerland)

The people of Belmont in Switzerland believed that
hens had long tongues and that the moon was made
of yellow Swiss cheese. They were distant cousins of
the men of Sainte-Dodo in France and the men of
Gotham in England, and they had little in their heads
to think with, and so they thought little.

Their village lay against a green mountain, and in
the summertime they sent their cows into the high
pastures to fatten. In the winter they watched the
holes in their big, round cheeses and sat in their snug
homes by the roaring fire in the stoves and made
brown cuckoo clocks. They led very happy lives.

Now, in that village there was a pretty little church
where young and old went every Sunday to pray to the

Lord. Next to the church was God's acre—that is, the cemetery. After a time, the stones in the cemetery were getting so close to the church that the people decided to move the church off a way, and so make more room for the cemetery.

They thought about it for a time and then decided to move the church about three yards away.

They measured off the distance.

"How shall we mark the spot?" they asked.

The mayor scratched his head, thought, and then said:

"I know how. It's a hot day, too hot to work in our leather jackets. Why don't we take them off and lay them out along the line our church is to reach? This will tell us exactly where we are to stop."

Everyone thought that was a fine idea. Off went the leather jackets, and they laid them out in a long line in the grass—the line up to which they intended to push the church.

"And now to work, good men of Belmont," the mayor cried. "Come, we all must work with a good will."

The mayor marched at the head in military step, and all the villagers—men, women, and children—followed him. Thus they came to the eastern wall of the church.

"Now, every man, woman, and child, put your

shoulders against the church wall and push with all your might."

Every man, woman, and child did exactly as the mayor ordered. Each put his shoulder against the wall and set his feet hard on the ground.

"Every time I cry, 'One,' you push," the mayor shouted. "First take a deep breath." They all did. "Now—One!" and everyone pushed and strained until they were red in the face.

"One!" the mayor roared again, and again they pushed, holding their breath.

The mayor kept on shouting "One!" and the Belmont folk kept on pushing until the perspiration ran down their faces and their bones began to ache.

Meanwhile some young fellows, passing through the town, stopped at the unusual sight of seeing folks trying to push a church.

"Oh, it's only the folks of Belmont," one said. "They are known in all Switzerland for their foolishness."

They shrugged their shoulders and went on. A few steps more and they saw the jackets in the grass.

"Here are fine leather jackets no one wants," one of the fellows said with a wink in his eyes.

"That's true," said another. "Otherwise why would they be left where anyone passing would take them?"

"If we don't take them, someone else will," said a third, "so we might as well."

They took the jackets and went their way merrily.

The Belmont folks were pushing and pushing until their breath came very heavy, while the sun rose higher and it was getting hotter.

"Maybe we have pushed the church far enough," the mayor said. "Let's stop." They did, wiping their foreheads.

"Let us see if we reached the line where we left our jackets," said the mayor.

They walked to where they had left their jackets.

No jackets were there!

"Where can our jackets be?" they cried.

"Perhaps someone took them."

"*Diable!* No!" cried the mayor. "We pushed the church too far, and now the church covers our jackets."

The men of Belmont lost their jackets, but they wept no tears for them. On the contrary, they were happy that their coats were covered by their church, and they were proud they were strong enough to move the church so far.

"Here are fine jackets no one wants," one of the fellows
said with a twinkle in his eye.

50. LUTONYA

(Russia)

In deep Russia there were once an old man and an old woman who were far from smart. They were real *duraks*—that is, sillies. But they had a son who was smart as a bird. His name was Lutonya.

One day the old woman was bringing a big log from the shed to the *iszba*.* She stumbled along the yard because there were deep ruts from the rain. She stepped into one of them and the log dropped on her feet. Bang! The woman began to cry. The tears flowed from her eyes as from a river.

"Holy Volga! What a terrible misfortune! What a terrible thing it would be to drop a log like that on a child. It would lose its life!

* *Iszba* is a hut used as house and home.

235

"Suppose it was our grandchild! Suppose our dear son, Lutonya, were married and he had a son, my grandson. I would rock his cradle and I would need a log for the fire. I would bring in a log and it would drop on our sweet, young grandson and would crush out his life! What a misfortune!" She wept worse than before, wringing her hands in despair.

Her husband came up to her and asked, "What are you crying about?"

She told him.

"That is truly a terrible misfortune and punishment," he said, and he, too, began to cry bitter tears.

Lutonya, their brave son, came out and asked, "What are you two crying for, Mother?"

"Oh, what a terrible misfortune, brave Lutonya. Do you see this log?"

"I do."

"If you were married and if your wife had a fine son and I would carry a log to the stove and the log would fall out of my hands over his cradle just as this log did, right on the innocent child, it would cripple him forever or maybe even crush out its innocent life!" And she cried even harder.

"It would be a terrible misfortune!" said the old man, and he, too, wept worse than before.

Lutonya listened and looked and then he said:

"My dear father and mother, for many years I have

listened to these tales in our home and they are very silly. Now I am leaving home to wander in the world, and I won't come back until I find folks who are even sillier than that."

He made a bundle of bread and salt, took his stick in his hand, and set off through the world. He walked and he walked over roads and paths. Soon he came to a place where two carpenters were building an *iszba*. All the logs on the sides were put up except one on which they would put the roof. That last log was too short and each carpenter was holding one end of the log and pulling as hard as he could to stretch it.

"What are you doing, brothers?" asked Lutonya.

"We are trying to stretch this log so that it will fit on the top. We have been pulling it for hours, but the log is still the same size."

"Ah, you must be cousins to my father and mother. Come, I'll show you a way out of your trouble."

He took a short log, nailed it to the log they were trying to stretch, and it fitted just right.

The carpenters thanked him and blessed him and gave him cool *kvas** to drink, and Lutonya went on walking through the land.

"These two *duraks* are as silly and even sillier than my father and mother," he said.

He walked on the roads and he walked on the paths

* A pleasant, soury, fermented apple drink.

and he came to a meadow where a peasant was standing behind a horse, trying to push it into a horse collar another peasant was holding.

"Hail, brothers! God bless you! What are you doing?" Lutonya asked.

"We are on our way to Bryansk to get a load of wood on our wagon. We sat down for a rest and let the horse graze. Now we want to go on, and we want to put the horse into the collar to hitch it to the wagon. But some witch has gotten into that animal—it just won't move."

"You surely must be cousins to my father and mother," he said. "Come, I'll show you how to do it, and you'll be able to go on your way."

He put the collar on the horse, and they hitched it to the wagon and went on, thanking him and blessing him.

"These two fool drivers are even sillier than my father and mother," Lutonya said and set off.

He traveled over hills and through valleys, and in the evening he came to an *iszba* where two who had just married lived in peace. They asked Lutonya to sit down and eat with them. He thanked them and sat at the table.

"Wife, I would like some milk," said the young master to the housewife.

The young wife took a spoon and went down into the cellar and came up with milk in it, which she poured into the glass. Then she went down into the cellar again and came up with another spoonful of milk. Then she went down again, bringing the spoonful of milk once more. She kept on going into the cellar, bringing up each time one spoonful of milk and pouring it into the glass.

"Do you always bring the milk from the cellar by the spoonful?" asked Lutonya.

"My wife has done that since we were married," the young husband said proudly. "She isn't the lazy kind."

"You must be cousins to my father and mother," Lutonya said. "I'll show you a new way of bringing your milk from the cellar to the table. Give me an earthen pitcher."

The young wife did, and when he went down into the cellar she followed him. He filled the pitcher with the milk and took it up.

"Now," he said, "you won't have to go down to the cellar so often. It will save your feet."

Both the young people gave him thanks as high as heaven and said they were very happy to learn the new way of bringing milk from the cellar to the table.

The next morning Lutonya turned his steps homeward.

"These two young *duraks* are as silly and even sillier than my father and mother. Maybe I should be satisfied in my own home."

Lutonya said the words and did the deed and went home.

There he found his father and mother the same as ever—and weren't they glad to see him!

51. THE TALE OF THE MEN OF PRACH

(Yugoslavia)

There are many islands along the Dalmatian Coast, which is in Yugoslavia, and all kinds of people live there. Some are wise and some "otherwise," like the people of the island of Prach. The people of Prach weren't wise, but "otherwise." That is, they were plain silly—Noodleheads—but they were ambitious.

"If we had a bigger harbor for our ships we would be richer," said the merchants.

"If we had more islands near us, the fish couldn't run away from our nets," said the fishermen.

"If the fishermen would catch more fish, the merchants would do more business, and we would sell more grain and lambs," said the farmers.

So each one wished for more islands, and in the end they held a council about the matter. All agreed that they must have at least one more island near Prach.

In the end one wise old man spoke up.

"There is that big island not far out in the sea. Why don't we pull it near ours, and then everyone will be satisfied."

Everyone thought this a fine idea. The question was: how to pull the island, far out in the sea, nearer their own.

A young fisherman said it could be done by putting all the boats against the edge of that island when the wind was blowing strong, and then the wind would push the boats and the island toward Prach. But the old sailors said that might damage their good boats. After hours of talk, it was decided that the best thing would be to pull the island toward theirs with a strong, thick rope. They would tie the rope around the island with a thick knot, with the long end at Prach, where everybody would pull with all his strength until the island was near enough.

The rope was made, it was tied around the island, and the long end reached Prach.

On a day, at a set hour, all the Prach folk got hold of that rope, the mayor directing, and everyone pulled so hard they got red in the face.

The rope began to stretch.

"Ha!" the men shouted. "The rope is stretching. The island is coming nearer. Pull harder!"

They did; the rope gave a little more.

"It's stretching! The island is getting nearer! Huzzah! Pull harder! Pull! Pull!"

Pull they did, harder and harder and then—crack! The rope ripped apart. Every Pracher, man, woman, and child, fell backward to the ground.

"Glory to the Saints!" the old wise men shouted. "The rope broke! And the island is nearer . . . near enough." And this satisfied the men of Prach, and they told all the Yugoslavians about it. And the Yugoslavians laughed and just said, "Prach! Noodleheads!"

52. SMARTNESS FOR SALE

(Yugoslavia)

There was another island in the Adriatic Sea, near Yugoslavia, where people were very simple. They were so simple they believed the sun rose from the sea when the cocks crowed on the farms and went to sleep in the sea when the chickens put their heads under their wings.

These island folk would have been very happy if Yugoslavians nearby hadn't laughed at them so much.

Folks far and wide said they were Noodleheads, and that made them unhappy. They held long discussions at their town meetings—how they could become clever and smart so they would be like all other Yugoslavians and no one would laugh at them.

One time an old man spoke up: "I know we are simple folk and smart folk laugh at us because we are simple. These smart ones must buy their smartness somewhere. When you buy honey, eating is sweet. I suppose smartness is for sale in the big cities where they live. Why can't we buy it in the same place?

"I say we should collect fifty gold pieces in our village and send our three strongest men to a big city, perhaps even to Split, and there buy us enough smartness for the whole village."

Everyone thought that was a fine idea. So they got together fifty gold pieces, chose the three strongest men in town, and told them to go to the big city to buy either pounds or barrels of smartness—whichever way it was sold, so there would be enough for the whole village.

The three took a large boat and set out for Split. They came to the harbor, got out, and went into the city to the big marketplace. They spoke to many merchants, asking each one if he had smartness and cleverness and wisdom for sale. The merchants laughed and sent them from one to another. In the end, they spoke to a merchant who was a rogue and liked a good joke.

"You've come to the right man," said he. "I deal in smartness, wit, and wisdom. But these commodities cost a lot of money. Have you plenty with you?"

"We have fifty pieces of gold. Will that be enough to buy smartness for our whole village?"

"That will be just right. Come tomorrow and I'll have enough smartness and wisdom for your whole village."

They went to the inn, satisfied.

The merchant got a small mouse trap, caught a small mouse, and put it in. The next day he met the three strong men of the island.

"Out with your money, I have your merchandise."

They gave him the fifty gold pieces.

"Look," he said, holding out the little trap all covered up. "In this trap there is enough smartness and wisdom for your whole village. It will make everyone as smart as anyone in Yugoslavia. Guard it well and don't open it until you reach your island. When you get there, open it and let out the wisdom in it, and everyone there will be as smart as the smartest in the land."

The men were pleased, thanked the merchant, and went back to their boat.

They set sail on the blue Adriatic, where every island is beautiful as a pearl.

While the three were sailing with the wind they were talking of this and that. Said the biggest of the three: "It isn't good for all people to be equally smart in this world. Some people have to be smarter than others, just as some trees are bigger than others. That is the way the Lord God made the world. And just for that reason it wouldn't be good for every person on our island to be as smart as every other person."

The other two shook their heads and agreed.

"We can't do things as wisely as the Lord," they said, "so we'll have to leave things as they are."

"No, we won't," said the first one. "I know a remedy. Let us three take half the treasure of smartness for ourselves, and the rest we can give to our village. Let us do it right now."

They opened the door of the trap just the least little bit, but the mouse was very small and ran out and hid in the ship. The mouse was so small it looked just like a gray streak that these three took for smartness. They shouted and screamed, but the shouting and the screaming did not do any good.

They sat down to talk over what to do next.

Then the one who had had the idea of taking half the smartness for the three said:

"Aren't we sillies? Truly we deserve that name. Isn't the smartness still on our boat? It couldn't run away out into the sea, so it must still be here." That satisfied the others.

When they got to the island, the people of the village were there in their best clothes to meet them.

They told them they had bought a boatful of smartness—enough for every man, woman, and child.

"How can we get it?" the men asked.

That was a new problem, and they decided to hold a meeting about it at once. There was talk to fill the Adriatic Sea, and in the end the problem was solved.

It was decided to drag the boat onto the shore and tie it to the trees and put a guard around it, so that the smartness in it couldn't run away and couldn't be stolen. Whenever anyone needed some of it for work or trading, he would go onto the boat and get it. This way the islanders would be as smart as anyone in Yugoslavia.

And that's what happened!

53. THE MOON IN THE DONKEY

(Spain)

In the proud land of Spain, there was, many years ago, a little village up in the mountains that few people ever visited for many reasons. The most important was that these villagers were so different from the rest of the Spaniards, you would think they came from the moon.

If people of other villages said something was blue, they said it was green—and green it was to them, no matter what the rest of the world said.

Now, a farmer in that village had a gray donkey that was a true Spanish donkey. He did as he pleased and believed that whatever he did was right.

One beautiful evening the donkey decided he

wanted to take a walk through the village. He went from his stall to the door, nozzled it until it opened, went out, and strolled through the street. In the sky a full moon shone large and yellow, and clouds were playing games, blowing in all directions.

The good people of the village were sitting at their doors, talking of their affairs. No one minded the donkey, for he was known to everyone. Soon Master Long Ears felt thirsty.

In the center of the village was a small pond, and to it the donkey went to drink. He dipped his wet nose into the water and began drawing it up in loud, slirfing sounds.

The full, yellow moon in the sky had a fine counterpart in the shimmering, rippling water. Some villagers were sitting right at the pond's edge, watching the drinking donkey, watching the moon in the water, and worrying lest the donkey drink up the moon.

Suddenly a large, black cloud came along the sky. It came up to the moon, floated across, and—the moon was gone!

"The donkey drank up the moon!" the villagers sitting there shouted.

The moon no longer shone in the street, and those sitting at their doors and at the inn took up the cry.

"The donkey drank up the moon!"

"Arrest the culprit!"

"Put him in jail!"

Everyone was shouting and running in all directions in the dark. The policeman of the village came rushing from his home.

"There is the vagabond!" "The culprit who drank up the moon!" "Arrest him!"

The officer took the donkey by his ears and led him to the village prison. The villagers followed, jeering the animal that had committed the crime.

The donkey spent the night in prison, and the next morning he was brought before the judge. All the village was there to see that the criminal received his proper punishment.

Those who had sat at the pond accused the donkey of having drunk up the moon. They swore they had seen it with their own eyes.

Even a little boy said, "I saw the moon floating in the pond, and then that bad donkey came up and began to drink, and soon he drank up all the moon."

After that the judge asked for no more witnesses.

Now they had to decide the punishment for that culprit. Some said one thing, some another. There was no end of words. It was not an easy matter to agree on the punishment for such a great crime.

Then one old man arose. He had lived many years and had traveled even to Madrid. Everyone listened to him with respect.

"It is a great calamity that has befallen our village," said he. "Every village in Spain will have a moon, and what will we have? An ass that swallowed the moon! Such a disgrace we cannot permit.

"Noble neighbors, we must get that moon back. It is better to be without a donkey than without a moon. That donkey swallowed the moon, so the moon must be in the donkey. Therefore, let us open that donkey and get the moon out. Then we will have light at night, just like every other village of Spain."

The villagers cheered the old gentleman, and everyone agreed it was the wisest counsel of all.

So it was done.

And that is how that little village, full of fine, proud Spaniards, got their moon to shine on them once again!

54. NOT ON THE LORD'S DAY

(Portugal)

There was a little village in Portugal where folks had heads soft as butter. They stumbled over a straw and carried water in sieves. In short, they were Noodle-heads.

One day two young people of that village were to be married. Come Sunday morning, they dressed in their finest clothes, full of color and fancy, and got their mules ready with silvered saddles and red and yellow bangles. All the townsfolk were in their finest, too. Everyone was gay as the birds and they set out for the church.

It was a hot day and it took time, but in the end they came to the church door. Bride and groom were in high spirits, sitting on their mules, and so was all the company behind them. So happy were the bride and groom, they forgot where they were sitting and tried to go into the church mounted on the mules. Of course they couldn't, because the door was not high enough.

They stopped in great surprise and so did all the company. They had gone to church every Sunday and they had always gone in without any trouble. Why couldn't they today? They did not know that he who rides on a camel needs a very big gate.

They looked at the door. It seemed so much below them. What had happened?

"We always came to church, ever since we were children, and always could get in. Why not today?" the groom said with a puzzled face.

"Perhaps the good Lord doesn't want you two to be married," said a villager.

"Silly," cried the mother of the bride.

Alas! Having long hair and short brains, no one thought that the young couple couldn't get into the church because they were sitting on the high mules.

Talk went on a mile a minute and words flew around like sparrows. In the end one wise man said:

"There are two ways of solving this problem of getting the bride and groom into the church. The first is to cut off the heads of the bride and the groom, and the second, to cut off the legs of the mules."

Everyone thought the old man very wise; the only question was which of his suggestions to follow. Some were in favor of the heads, and others were in favor of the legs. The villagers were about equally divided in their opinions, and so the arguments went on a long time.

The priest waiting inside the chapel was getting impatient, and hearing the commotion he came outside and asked them the cause of the waiting.

Everyone shouted at once, trying to tell him the trouble. It took some time for him to understand the argument. Then he said:

"Good people, this is the Lord's Day and must be observed according to the Bible, without many words or much labor. So today this problem must be solved differently. Instead of cutting off the heads of the young people or the legs of the good mules, I would say that the two should get off the mules instead, leave the beasts at the door, and come into the church on foot."

So it was done. The bride and the groom got off their mules, and so did all the other villagers. They all went into the church, where the young couple was married and lived happily ever after.

55. THE WOLF IN THE SACK

Sometimes sharp ones become silly ones.

A flock of sheep grazed in the meadow, but the shepherd was a lazy one who often went into the woods to play on his flute with his friends. The sheep knew this, and they also knew that there was a fierce wolf near, always watching to catch lone sheep when the shepherd was away. The sheep kept sharp eyes in all directions.

Soon they found the head of a dead wolf. It was a fierce-looking head. The eyes were glassy green and the tongue was hanging out on the side.

"What a terrible head!" cried the sheep. "We don't like to even look at it."

"Let us put it in a sack and keep it," said an old sheep. "You never can tell how we can use it."

So they put it into a sack and kept on grazing, dragging the sack behind them.

Soon the wolf came slinking along. He saw the shepherd wasn't there and was watching for a chance to get a lamb.

The sheep saw him and huddled together. But the old sheep who had put the wolf's head into the sack walked slowly alone toward the wolf.

"Good day, Brother Wolf," the sheep said.

"Good day, Brother Sheep," said the wolf. "I see the shepherd is away. He is a lazy fellow."

"Yes, our shepherd is lazy, but we can take care of ourselves, thank the Lord." Saying this, he dragged the sack nearer to the wolf for him to see it better.

"What have you in that sack? Is it a fat lambkin that isn't strong enough to walk?" asked the wolf.

"No, it's not a lamb, Brother Wolf. It's something I know you wouldn't like to see."

That made the wolf curious. "Of course I would like to see it," he said. "Is it something good to eat?"

"No, no. I better not even tell you what it is."

"Please tell me. I want to know."

"I really shouldn't. But since you beg so hard, I will. But, remember, if you don't enjoy the sight don't blame me. I warned you."

"I won't blame you. Come, show me. Quick!"

The old sheep untied the bag slowly while the wolf hopped around, nose down. When the bag was open, the sheep turned it around, and out fell the head of the dead wolf. It was a fearful sight.

"There you see it," the sheep said.

The wolf was shocked. "What's this," he growled. "Where did you . . . did you get this head?"

"It's a sad story, and I don't like to tell it to you because it's about one of your relatives. It's a very sad story, how that wolf lost the rest of himself."

"I'd like to know," the wolf growled, showing his fangs.

"If you really want to know I will tell you, but I swear to you we did not do this on purpose or because we wanted to."

"Who is *we?*" snarled the wolf.

"We were grazing peacefully, just as we are doing now, Brother Wolf, when along came the wolf whose head you see here on the ground. He was a whole wolf then and he tried to catch one of the young lambs to eat it. The mother of that lamb, and a few other mothers, leaped on that wolf and just tore him to pieces. You know how fierce a mother is when you try to rob her of her child. She becomes more fierce than a lion. What you see here is that poor wolf's head. We were taking it to bury it."

You know what happens when fear comes: reason runs away and foolishness comes in, and that wolf— you know the rest. His tail went between his legs and off he slunk, frightened silly, never to be seen again.

56. JUAN BOBO

(Puerto Rico)

In Puerto Rico they tell enough tales about Juan Bobo to fill the king's palace. There are long tales and short tales, but all the tales say that Juan Bobo was the worst Noodlehead who ever lived on that lovely island.

Juan Bobo's mother was a rich lady. She had lands and she had fine clothes, but there was one thing she did not have: a smart son. He was Juan Bobo, and he had as much wit in his head as a snake has legs.

One day Juan Bobo's mother dressed herself in her finest finery and said to her son:

"Juan Bobo, I am going to Mass. You watch the house and watch the pig tied to the post. Be sure to keep the pig out of the hot sun or it will get sick."

"Mother, I will watch the house and watch the pig. You go to Mass and don't worry. All will be well."

The mother went to Mass, and Juan Bobo stayed at home. The sun was moving in the sky and it was getting hotter and hotter, and the poor pig was standing in the hot sunshine.

Juan Bobo had forgotten what his mother had said, but he did hear the pig grunting more and more. Juan Bobo listened, then he said:

"Ah, I understand. You miss my mother and want to go to Mass with her. Come, I'll let you go, but first I must dress you clean as my mother dresses me when I go to church."

He untied the pig from the post and let it in the house. There he took out the finest dress and the finest shawl his mother had. Then he held the pig tight between his legs and began dressing it. The pig squealed and squirmed.

"Don't be such a stupid beast," Juan Bobo cried. "Here I am, putting my mother's finest clothes on you so that you look like a queen, and what do you do? You squirm and squeal as if someone were cutting your throat. Stop that."

The pig kept on squealing and squirming, and Juan Bobo had a hard time getting the dress on. He was angry because he thought the pig very unreasonable. When he was done he said:

"Here you are, dressed; now you can go find my mother." Then he gave the pig a kick and the pig raced out of the house.

The pig was very uncomfortable in the dress and shawl, and it ran wildly into a pool of water. The clothes were torn and all soaking wet, and the pig was squealing more than ever.

Right then the mother came home and saw the strange sight.

"Holy Saints! What has happened?" she cried.

"The pig cried that it wanted to go to you, Mother, and I couldn't let it go to church without dressing it properly so I put on it your dress and shawl. But that stupid beast was squealing all the time, and instead of going to you, it ran into the pond."

The mother cried, the mother scolded, the mother beat Juan Bobo, but do you think that changed him? Not in the least. He was just as foolish after that, if not worse, and kept on doing the Noodlehead deeds he had done all his life.

57. NOODLEHEAD PAT

(Canada)

In the days when the Irish had very little food in their own land, many of them came to Canada, where there was plenty of food and plenty of work.

Of all the Irish folk who came to the new land, there was just one who was not smart; the rest were smart enough to jump to the moon. Pat was his name, and people called him a dunce and a disgrace to the Irish race. I would have called him a Noodlehead. Every mother's son was forever making sport of Pat the Noodlehead.

One fine, soft day he was walking in the countryside where the birds were singing sweet as anything. There, from the opposite direction, came Mike, whistling a tune. When he saw Pat, he stopped. "Top o' the morning to you," said Mike.

"Top o' the morning to you," said Pat.

"And where may you be going?" asked Mike.

"I'm just walking along," said Pat.

"Walking along just like that?" said Mike.

"Aye, just like that, with nothing on my mind."

"Well, if you've nothing on your mind, Pat, here is something for you to do." You see, Mike thought he would have a little fun with Pat.

"I don't mind a bit doing something," said Pat.

"Well, then," said Mike, "I'll tell you what you can do. See that great gray stone on the side?"

"That I do, indeed," said Pat.

"Well, then, I'll put my hand on that stone and you can hit me with all your might, and you'll see it'll never hurt my hand the least bit."

"Now, how can that be?" said Pat.

"You'll see fast enough."

So Mike put his hand on the big gray rock, fingers spread out. It was hot, for the sun was shining on it. And silly Pat, he pulled his arm way back to get a strong swing with it. Then, using all the strength that was in him, he swung his fist at Mike's hand. But Mike pulled his hand away quickly, and Pat, he hit his fist on the hot gray stone.

"There you see, Pat," said Mike, a big grin on his red face, "I told you, you wouldn't hurt my hand the least bit."

"I see," said Pat, looking kind of puzzled. And, being the Noodlehead he was, he had nothing else to say and just walked off, rubbing his hurt fist. Mike went the other way, laughing to himself and wondering whether Pat truly was an Irishman or not.

Pat had not walked long when François came down the road. François had come from sunny France to live a better life in Canada, and he was the town cobbler. He spoke a little English.

"Top o' the morning to you," said Pat.

"Bonjour, Monsieur Pat. It's a fine morning."

"So it is, François. Would you like me to show you something funny?"

"I always like to see something funny," said François. What is it?"

"I will let you hit my hand as hard as you want, and you will see it won't hurt my hand at all."

"That I would like to see. It would be very funny."

Pat looked around for a rock, but there was none near.

"Well, if I can't find a rock, I can put my hand in another place just the same," Pat mumbled to himself. Then he put his hand on his own face, spreading his fingers just as Mike had done, and said, "Now, you hit my hand hard and you will see it won't hurt my hand the least bit."

François looked surprised. He knew Pat had little to spare in his head, but he could not understand what Pat wanted.

"You say I should hit your hand hard and it won't hurt you?"

"That's just what I said," said Pat. "Just you watch. It's a trick. You hit my hand hard and it won't hurt my hand in the least."

François saw that Pat was in earnest. He looked at the hand spread out over the face, he raised his fist and hit out. Right then Pat pulled his hand away, and François' fist landed on Pat's face. Pat was so surprised he did not feel any pain for a minute.

"Well," he said," . . . but I didn't have any pain on my hand!"

François looked at Pat, then he went his way, shaking his head.

Now I'll tell you one more tale about Noodlehead Pat.

In the old country Pat had slept on straw and hay. When he came to Canada, he heard folks talk about how fine it was to sleep on feather pillows.

One day when he was walking along the road, a duck's feather came flying in the wind.

"Oh, there's a fine feather. I must try sleeping on it to learn if what folks say is true."

He ran after that white feather, caught it, and held it tight between two fingers. Then he looked around, and saw a rock. He went over to the rock, laid the feather on it, stretched himself on the ground, and put his head on the feather on the rock.

For a time he lay still while the rock was digging into his head.

"Canada folks are foolish," he cried. "It's much better sleeping on sweetsmelling hay or even yellow dry straw than on a feather. If it's so hard sleeping on one feather, how much harder it would be to sleep on a pillow full of 'em."

That's the kind of thing Noodlehead Pat was doing and saying all his life in rich Canada.

58. THE SOMBREROS OF THE MEN OF LAGOS

(Mexico)

In gay Mexico there is a town called Lagos. The people of that town are famous throughout the sunny land for the silly things they say and the silly things they do. In fact, they are as silly as the men of Gotham in England or the men of Chelm in Poland.

Once there was a great argument whether the church of the town of Lagos should have four-cornered or three-cornered windows, and in the end it was decided to leave it to the judgment of the oldest and wisest men of the town.

There were twelve of these men then, and they decided to meet on the bench in the town square on the following Tuesday to discuss the important question.

Come Tuesday, six of the elders came first, each dressed in wide white pants and white shirts, with big, wide sombreros—that is, big wide straw hats—on their heads. The brims of those hats were so wide that two people could dance on them.

It was a hot day, so the six sat down on the long bench, took off their wide-brimmed sombreros, and put them right next to them. The brims of the sombreros took up more space than the men who sat next to them, so that the bench was all full.

The six old men sat silently, their wide hats beside them, waiting for the other six to come. Soon the other six came. They looked for space on the bench to sit down, but there wasn't any.

"There is no room on the bench for us," said one of those standing.

"No, there is no room for us," said another.

"I think the bench has shrunk," said one of those sitting.

"Yes, that's just what happened," said the others.

"Why don't we try and stretch the bench?" asked one of those who were sitting.

"That's a good idea, let us try it," said one standing.

The six sitting on the bench arose, put their sombreros on their heads, and got hold of one end of the bench. Then the six standing got hold of the other end of the bench. Then each group began pulling the wood as hard as it could. They did this for some time.

"Let us try and see if we stretched the wood," said the oldest of the twelve.

They put the bench down.

"We will know at once, if we can all sit on it now," spoke one.

All twelve sat down, each with his wide-brimmed sombrero on his head. Of course, now that the brims took up no space, there was plenty of room for all. They sat down, very pleased with themselves.

"Now that we have a done a fine job stretching that bench, we can discuss our problem," the oldest one said. So the men of Lagos went on to their discussion.

Do you see why the men of Lagos were famous in the land of Mexico?

59. THE "FOOLISH PEOPLE"

(U.S.A.)

The Apache Indians of North America tell tales about the "Foolish People." Other Indians call them "Spotted People." It's the same. They were just people who were very foolish and lived very poorly. They had no houses and few clothes; they did not even know what horses were.

One day, some of these Foolish People went on a raid and saw some horses.

"What kind of persons are they?" they asked one another.

No one knew.

"They carry four rocks on their feet," one said, looking at the hoofs.

"Let us take one to our camp," one said.

They did.

"What shall we give that person to eat?" they asked.

They gave him meat gravy. The horse wouldn't eat it.

They gave him meat. The horse wouldn't eat it.

They gave him coffee. The horse wouldn't drink it.

A Mescalero Apache Indian, who had married a woman from the Foolish People, came into the camp. He stood and watched what the Foolish People were doing.

"Don't you know what this is?" he asked.

"No, we don't," they answered.

"It's a horse."

"A horse!"

"Yes, a horse. You sit on it, and it takes you wherever you want to go, very fast. Faster than the fastest runner."

"What does a horse eat?"

"It eats . . ." The horse walked away and began to eat the grass.

"You see what a horse eats. It eats grass. Just let it go, and it will feed itself. But you must hobble its forelegs so that it doesn't run away."

Now the Foolish People knew what a horse was.

When it had eaten, one of the Foolish People

wanted to get on the horse and see how fast it could run, as the Mescalero Indian had said. He climbed on the horse, but sat backwards, looking at its tail. The horse walked forward and the Indian slid off. Everybody laughed. Most of all, the Mescalero Indian, who said:

"They call you the 'Foolish People' and it is the right name for you. You don't even know how to ride a horse. I'll show you how to do it."

He got on the horse the right way, and the horse raced with him on the plain.

"Ha," the Foolish People cried, "that Mescalero son-in-law has glue on his pants. He does not slide off a horse."

From then on, they knew how to ride on a horse.

60. LITTLE HEAD, BIG MEDICINE

(U.S.A.)

This is a night story Hopi Indians tell their young ones before sleeping-time, if they want them to have good dreams with laughter. It is a daytime story for white people when the sun is shining on the far, brown mountains of Arizona.

But before you hear it, I will tell you something you must know. The Indians believe that in the olden days animals, trees, birds, grass, earth, the moon and stars were people—they talked like people and acted like people. That is just what they do in the old Indian stories. If you remember that, you will laugh at them just as much as the Indians laugh at them.

On a warm day when the sky was clear and the cactus plants were bright, the Turtle people decided to climb out of the *bayupa*—that is, the Little Colorado River—where they lived. They wanted to go into the desert to hunt the fresh cactus plants they loved to eat. They all climbed slowly up the brown, sandy bank and began to crawl along the sandy earth. They walked this way and that way all over the deserty earth. All the turtles were there except Young Turtle, who was fast asleep and did not hear her people go away.

When Young Turtle got up she said:

"Where are the people? Where is my mother? Where is everybody?"

She looked all over, and when she came to the bank, she saw the tracks. Then she knew at once where everyone had gone, and she started out to find them.

Up the bank she climbed and began crawling— *crshsh, crshsh, crshsh.* She crawled for a long time, and then she became tired and lay down under a low, olive-colored bush and began to cry.

Along came Old Fox, hungry as always. This was a foolish fox and everyone knew it.

"You sing a pretty song. I like it. Go on, sing for me," he said.

"I am not singing, I am crying," said Young Turtle.

"Keep singing, I like to hear you sing."

"I am not singing, I am crying. I want to find my people."

"You better keep on singing," said red, hungry Fox, "or I'll eat you quick."

"I can't sing, and I can't stop crying, and I want my people." Young Turtle cried harder than ever.

"Well," said Old Fox, "if you won't sing for me, I'll eat you right now," and he looked at Young Turtle with angry eyes. He was getting madder and madder all the time, for he was very hungry.

Now, the Turtle people are never afraid. They don't run away, even from their enemies, but Young Turtle was so young, and she had heard so many bad stories about Fox, she was just a little scared. But she had a smart head on her thin neck and thought of something good.

"I am sorry, Fox, I can't sing, and so you'll have to eat me. But I want to tell you something: It won't hurt me the least bit if you eat me. When you swallow me I'll just live inside you the same as I live right here; it will be you who will hurt. For I have a very hard shell, I can tell you, and my hard shell will hurt you inside."

Fox thought about this and wrinkled his nose. He didn't like it, so he stood there saying nothing.

Then Young Turtle spoke again:

"I don't mind. Just go and eat me. I don't care if you do anything to me, only don't throw me into the river.

I don't like the cold water, and I am afraid I will drown."

Fox was madder than a tribe of hornets on the warpath. He was hungry, but he was afraid to eat Young Turtle, and that made him feel very mean. So he picked up Young Turtle in his mouth and ran over to the river and threw her into the water.

"There, that will teach you a lesson," he cried.

Young Turtle swam out, stuck out her thin neck, and cried, "Thank you, Friend Fox, for throwing me into the river. This is my home, and you saved me a long walk." Then she laughed and laughed.

That made Old Fox angrier than ever, and he jumped into the stream to catch Young Turtle. Water was running fast and carried Old Fox quickly down, and he was never seen again.

Young Turtle laughed every time she thought how she had tricked Old Fox. When her mother and her people came back, she told them what had happened, and all the turtles laughed and were proud of Young Turtle.

Said Mother Turtle: "I am proud of you because even though you are little in size, you already know big medicine, and that means that you are wise."

That's the story the Hopis tell their young ones to make them laugh and give them good dreams, and I hope it makes you smile, and have happy dreams.

61. SAM'L DANY, NOODLEHEAD*

(U.S.A.)

Sam'l Dany of Crawford County in Ohio was smart enough to make crows laugh.

One day Sam'l Dany went a-huntin', went in the woods to shoot deer, but it wasn't Sam'l Dany's huntin' day, same as no other day was.

He tramped 'round and 'round the woods till every creature knowed Sam'l Dany was out a-huntin', so they cropped grass and walked 'round him.

Deer and fox, hare an' bear, frolicked all 'round, but Sam'l Dany saw 'em no more than if he had pun'kin eyes.

* See *Sand in the Bag and Other Folk Stories of Ohio, Indiana, and Illinois,* by M. A. Jagendorf. Published by The Vanguard Press.

"What's the use o' huntin' when there ain't no game 'round?" He sat and ate his bread and meat.

The wood creatures lay a-restin', too, there was a still zoomin' in the dark woods, and Sam'l thought it a good time for stealin' a wink o' sleep. So he lay down on the good earth and soon was dreamin' of angels bringin' sizzlin' deer his way.

When the sun was gettin' low and the wind was blowin' warm, he got up.

"Time's ripe fer goin' home an' fer the evenin' meal. Night huntin' ain't no good fer a Christian man."

He set one foot afore the other, his nose straight in the front the way to home.

The more he walked, the more he seemed to walk. There was no end to that walkin', and he was no nearer to home. 'Twas gettin' darker all the time.

"I'm lost, sure's cookin'," cried Sam'l Dany, and he began shoutin' and runnin' and shoutin' and runnin'. But with all the shoutin' and runnin' he didn't seem to get any nearer to home. He was gettin' all tuckered out and near cryin', for 'twas now near dark all over the place.

All at once he saw signs pointin' to a farm, felt a foot-path under his feet, felt broken branches like made by passin' cattle. Sure 'nuf, there was a barn risin' out of the twilight, with buckets and wheelbarrows outside. He saw a chicken house with a door hangin' loose, a cabin with chinks wide open, and a broken fence. Looked kind o' familiar.

A woman in a calico dress was standin' at the fence lookin' anxious all 'round.

"Good evenin,' good woman," cried Sam'l Dany. "Know this neck o' the woods?"

"Know it good 's the palm o' my hand."

"Know perhaps where Sam'l Dany's cabin is?"

"Know it good 's the face in my head."

"Know Sam'l Dany?"

"Know 'm fer the biggest, silliest fellow in all O-hi-o."

"Can y' tell me where his cabin is?"

"Lan' sakes! Knew you were a fool, Sam'l Dany, but didn't know y' were such a big fool not t' know yer own home an' wife."

"Comin' t' think of it, this is my own cabin, an' you're my own wife that's a-talkin' t' me. I'm mighty glad t' find ye, for I'd lost my way an' sure thought I'd have t' sleep in the dark woods the night long. 'Deed the good Lord 's kind t' me."

Sam'l Dany was happy as a cricket in a chimney. He went into his cabin, had mush and milk for supper, and slept with a clear conscience.

Now, don't y' think Sam'l Dany was smart 'nuf to make crows laugh?

62. NOODLEHEAD LUCK

(U.S.A.)

A long time ago there lived a man in Massachusetts in the United States, named Lord Timothy Dexter. He was such a big gunsel, such a Noodlehead, that not only did the Commonwealth of Massachusetts laugh at him, but all the other New England states as well. He was a little fellow and wore a long jacket and tight breeches and he had a funny little dog.

He built himself a great palace with many statues. How did he get the money? In the noodliest way in the world.

In those days folks used heating pans in their beds to keep them warm on cold nights. Now, there was a merchant who had bought too many of those warming pans, and no one would buy them from him. The merchant needed money and wanted to sell them cheap. But neither rich nor poor would buy those pans because everyone had plenty of them on hand. So who do you think did buy them? No other than Noodlehead Lord Timothy Dexter. Everybody laughed at him; every merchant said he was crazy. And they laughed at him even more, and said he had wheels in his head, and was altogether bakeheaded, when he sent the warming pans to be sold in the hot West Indies.

"Who would buy warming pans in the West Indies where it is hot enough to boil eggs in the sunshine?" they asked.

But Noodlehead Lord Timothy Dexter sent them there just the same on his good ship, *Mehitabel.*

The ship came to port, and the folks in the West Indies looked at the shining heating pans with the long handles.

"They will make fine pans in which to boil our molasses," they shouted all together. And they paid Lord Timothy a good price for them.

So Noodlehead Lord Timothy Dexter made a big profit, as Noodleheads sometimes do.

Another time some merchants told Dexter to load his ships with coal and send them to Newcastle in

England, where there was more coal than in any other part of England.

Noddy Timothy loaded his ship with coal and sent it to Newcastle.

With Noodlehead luck it so happened that the coal mines of England were all shut at the time and English folks needed coal as much as they needed bread. So Lord Timothy Dexter's coal was bought at a great profit to him.

This is the way that Noodlehead was always doing daffy deeds. But those who were always wanting to make sport of him found that, with Noodlehead luck, he always won out in the end.

63. JOHN IN THE STOREROOM

(U.S.A.)

Once, many, many years ago, there was a woman in Louisiana who had a very stupid son. He was so stupid people called him Jean Sot—that is the French for John, the fool. And he sure was a fool, as big a Noodle-head as you could find anywhere in all the world.

One day the old mother said:

"Jean Sot, my son, I am old and must walk with a cane and I don't feel so well. Go to the pantry and bring me one of the bottles of wine standing on the shelf. A little wine will do me good. Be sure you don't break the bottle."

Jean Sot went to the storeroom and there were the bottles of wine standing in a row like soldiers. He picked one out.

"Maybe it is a good idea to smell the wine first to make sure it has not turned into vinegar," he said aloud.

He opened the bottle, smelled it, and it did not smell like vinegar.

"I better taste it to make sure it's good enough for my mother," he said.

So he took a sip.

"It tastes good, and I am sure my mother will like it. I like it, too. I'll take another sip."

He took a long sip and it tasted better than before. It made him feel nice and warm all over.

"That taste feels like another taste," he said. So he took another long sip.

"Each time I take a taste, it tastes better. I better keep on tasting until I find the best taste of all."

He kept on tasting and sipping and sipping and tasting until there wasn't a drop left. By then he felt so gay and warm he was singing and even dancing a little.

In the corner of the storeroom lived a goose. She had made a nest there, where she hatched her eggs.

When the goose saw Jean Sot dancing and waving his hands, she got a little frightened. Or maybe she thought she would join in the song and dance. She began quacking and flapping her wings and flying around.

Jean Sot, seeing the big white bird with wings wide-stretched, thought it was a ghost; he got hold of that "ghost" around the neck until it was very, very quiet. Then he threw the "ghost" away. He was tired now, so he sat down on the nest.

Jean's mother had been wondering why it was taking her son so long, so she hobbled in to see.

There was the old goose silently dead; there was her son, Jean Sot, sitting on the eggs.

"Where is my wine? Why do you sit on the goose's nest, and why did you kill our goose?" the mother cried.

"Mother, I just wanted to taste your wine to make sure it was not sour; before I knew it, there was no wine in the bottle. I thought the goose was a ghost who was going to tell you what I had done, so I finished him so he couldn't talk. Now he is dead, and you will never know that I drank the wine. And I am sitting here because I am tired."

"There is no one more stupid then you in all Louisiana, maybe not in all the world. Never again will I send you for wine," said the mother. And she didn't.

64. KIBBE'S SHIRT

(U.S.A.)

In the early days of hard New England, there lived a
very silly man and his name was Kibbe. Kibbe was
silly and Kibbe was chickenhearted. Some folks called
him a jelly bean and others called him plain Noodlehead, and he deserved all these names and then some
more.

One Sabbath day there was a great cry in Kibbe's
town that the Indians were coming.

Kibbe grabbed his gun and ran into the woods to
get his cow, which he prized more than anything else
he owned. He took his gun along, even though folks in
New England were not allowed to shoot on Sundays.

Soon after, there were two banging shots in the

woods, and Kibbe came running out shouting, "Indians! Indians! They shot me."

All the settlers ran into the woods in search of Indians, but, search as they would, there was no sign of Indians anywhere.

Said one: "Kibbe, are you sure you saw Indians?" He knew Kibbe had little in his head and would say things that were not so.

"They shot me! Two times," he said.

"Where did they shoot you?"

"In my back, and then I ran."

The men looked at Kibbe's shirt. There, indeed, were two holes made by gun shots, but Kibbe was not hurt anywhere. "This is very strange," an elder said. "Here are two holes from gun shots, but Kibbe has no sign of a wound."

"Of course I have no wounds," said Kibbe.

"You are shot and have no wounds? That is the strangest thing I ever heard," said another.

"How could I have a wound when I did the shooting myself?"

"You did the shooting yourself?"

"That's just what I did."

"Why?"

"Well, you see, when I came out into the woods to look for my cow, there were two deer as fine as ever you saw. Well, I wanted to shoot those deer, but I knew it was against the law to shoot on the Sabbath. So I shot them through my shirt, and then you wouldn't know, and you would think Indians shot at me!"

What could the village folks say? After all, it was Kibbe, and you cannot punish a man too much for being a nitwit.

NOTES

NUMBERS 1, 2, 3, 4.

All these tales from INDIA, and many others as well, I heard at the festive gatherings of people from India—students, artists, newspapermen, and diplomats at the United Nations, as well as in India House and International House in New York City. Undoubtedly all of them are in print, probably in somewhat different versions.

The story *The Horse-Egg* is popular not only in India but all over the world. There are many more episodes to this tale. The first European version of it is by the Italian Jesuit missionary, Beschi (1700-1742).

Don't Marry Two Wives is known and much liked all over the East. It is also found in the Hebrew Talmud. (In that version, one wife pulls out all the white hair, and the other all the black hair, leaving the foolish husband completely bald.)

The Noodlehead Tiger is told here a little differently than by Mr. L. Dames in his collection of Balochi Tales in *Folk-*

lore, Volume 4. There the tiger is in the jungle that is in-habited by jackals. As I heard it, it was inhabited by different animals—which shows how folk stories change in the telling.

The same popularity applies to *There Are Such People.* I believe I have read over twenty different versions of this story from as many different lands.

Let me add here that just as these stories from India have parallels in many lands, the same can be said of practically all the stories in this book.

NUMBERS 5, 6, 7.

"As old as in the day of *Hierokles*" was a common expres-sion in the days of the GREEKS, two thousand years ago. So these little tales—*Do You Know? Barefoot in Bed,* and *The Donkey of Abdera*—which were told in the days of that writer, were very old even then. From their similarity to Indian tales, there is no question but that these stories had been traveling around for hundreds—no, for thousands—of years before.

Punishing a donkey for misdeeds, real and imaginary, has been told in many other countries. The donkey has played an important part in the law and literature of the world, begin-ning with pre-Biblical days.

NUMBERS 8, 9, 10, 11.

All these JEWISH tales I heard in my early youth when I lived in Austria and traveled in Rumania, Poland, and some parts of Hungary and Russia. Then stories were the main source of entertainment.

I had a teacher in those early days whom I loved and whom I visited every Saturday afternoon when there was no class, when he would tell me stories. He was Polish and had come to Austria, where life was easier.

There is in these stories a wise and winking humor, which is wholly their own.

I suppose that they are in print somewhere, but such stories are so good they can be told over and over again.

NUMBER 12.

I found the SYRIAN donkey story in an unusual book called *Laughable Stories,* collected by Mar Gregory John Bar-Hebraeus, (1226-1286), and translated by E. A. Wallis Budge.

NUMBER 13.

The ARABIAN tale is the typical silly-husband and silly-wife episode found all over the world and in every collection of folk stories. I heard it at a gathering at the United Nations.

NUMBER 14.

CEYLON Noodlehead tales, though of the well-known pattern, are very amusing. They were originally collected by C. J. R. Mesurier and published in *The Orientalist* (1884). W. A. Clouston, of course, mentions them in *The Book of Noodles.*

They have a particularly charming pastoral simplicity, giving a feeling of farm life.

NUMBERS 15, 16.

These two CHINESE tales have been told many times. They both contain a wise and gentle and sly humor characteristic of many Chinese tales, and not easily found in others. I heard them first from Evan Esar, who is a very storehouse of world humor. He told me they are to be found in E. D. Edwards' *The Dragon Book.* Subsequently they were told to me by a Chinese student at Columbia working for his law degree.

NUMBERS 17, 18.

I don't think there is any country in the world where the AFRICAN story, *When Noodlehead Marries Noodlehead,* is not found. I chose the African version after L. Reinisch to show how differently it is told in Africa.

The Foolish Lion and the Silly Rooster is based on the folktale *The Fowl and the Lion,* found in the Bantu Studies VS—No. 4, 1931, and used with the permission of the managing editor of the University of the Witwatersrand, Johannesburg, South Africa.

NUMBER 19.

This PERSIAN story is told in all lands. I have heard it in Scotland, in Spain, and in Austria. The particular version was told to me in America at a U.N. party of Eastern people.

NUMBERS 20, 21.

I first heard these two JAPANESE tales in New York. Then I read a little book of fine regional Japanese folktales by Professor Kunio Yanagita, who graciously gave me permission to use any of his valuable work I desired.

Kettles have played an important part in the life of folk all over the world. A tale similar to *Magic! Silly Magic!* I found in Finland and among the North American Indians, where Coyote has a kettle boiling over a fire that is deep in the ground, telling people that the rays of the sun make it boil.

The Farmer's Secret is a type of story known in Europe, too. I was told that in Japan there are other versions of this tale.

NUMBERS 22, 23.

TURKISH hodja stories, and all sorts of other Turkish tales, I heard in the homes of my good Turkish friends Adnan Saygun, Emin Hekimgil, and others, when I was in Turkey.

There are endless hodja tales, and in them is the essence and flavor of the humor and wisdom of the East. Even the two examples here show how humor can be so flavored with wisdom that it is hard to tell where one begins and the other ends.

The Wisdom of the Lord was interestingly transformed when it was adopted by the Spanish folk of Mallorca. Here St. Peter suggests to the Lord that pumpkins should be on acorn trees—until an acorn falls on his head.

NUMBER 24.

This unusual SOUTH AMERICAN tale was told to me by a South American newspaperman at the U.N. He said he had heard it when he was in school.

The second part of the story of trying to fly sounds like a Tyll Ulenspiegel tale and probably could be traced to Euro-pean origin.

NUMBERS 25, 26, 27.

ENGLAND is rich in Noodleheads and Noodle towns. The tales of the Wise Men of Gotham are so well known that they need no introduction.*

Austwick in Yorkshire was as famous locally as Gotham was internationally, and *The Brave Men of Austwick* has a familiar Gothamite ring.

When I told my good friend Warrant Officer William B. Springle, who was my "folklore guide" in England in 1956, that I was on the lookout for Noodlehead stories, he told me there were endless traditional and current stories of that kind in the British Army. Only here they were called Knuckle-heads. He gave me a great many, and here are two examples. Many of them sounded very familiar, and I am certain were "adopted" stories.

* See *The Merry Men of Gotham,* The Vanguard Press, New York, N. Y.

NUMBER 28.

A Sheep Can Only Bleat is a typical Gotham-Scottish story.
(The Wise Man of Gotham sends the trivet home because it
has "three" legs and the Wise Man of Scotland sends the wheel
home because it turns.) I heard it in Scotland in the summer of 1956.

NUMBER 29.

In the same year, I traveled through Ireland and came to a
little village of Adare, "the most beautiful village in Ireland"
—and truly it deserves the name.

After unpacking, I walked through the village and wandered into a small pub—just a small dark room with a few
bottles on a shelf and before it, on a chair, a genial short man
with a moon-face. After a few moments we were in friendly
conversation and I told him I was traveling for pleasure and
for the pleasure of hearing the fine tales of Ireland. There
were two other men in the room, and soon we were swapping
tales. I told tall Western tales and tales of Johnny Darling
of the Catskill Mountains, and I was rewarded with Irish
tales. Here is one.

NUMBERS 30, 31, 32.

I have traveled from one end of FRANCE to the other many
times and I have heard many, many French tales. In 1954
I spent much time in the Dordogne district, and there I heard
stories from Jean Delteil and others with whom I spent hours
of delightful conversation, enjoying perhaps the most beautiful scenery in France.

Sainte-Dodo was as famous in France as Gotham was in
England, and the Wise Men of Dodo are well known everywhere in France—in Gascony in particular.

The "Tartari-Barbari" story I heard in a garbled version, and so I followed the L. Pineau 1891 recording. It is very much like our own tall tales in North America.

The story of Pierre Patelin, *Bahhh!* is a very famous one and has been known for over a thousand years. A farce based on the tale is the finest farce known.

NUMBER 33.

This DANISH tale belongs to the very popular class of silly sons and silly husbands. *Peter's Adventures* form a cycle of tales popular all over the world. This story I have known since childhood, and it was told to me again when I was last in Denmark.

NUMBER 34.

Faithful Legs and Lazy Head, the GYPSY story, was told by the famous gypsy storyteller, Johan Dimitri Taikon* to C. H. Tillhagen, who in turn told it to me.

My daughter told me she had either read or heard a story somewhat like it when she was in public school.

NUMBER 35.

When I was in Stockholm, Sweden, I was telling American folk stories, and the good Swedish folk and folklorists came back with Nordic Noodles, among them many from ICE-LAND. *The Man, the Woman, and the Fly* as I heard it is slightly different from the version of the *Tale of the Butter Tub* by Jon Arnason, translated by G. E. J. Powell and E. Magnusson. Here there is no king or queen as the printed version has.

---

* See *The Gypsies' Fiddle,* by M. A. Jagendorf and C. H. Tielhagen. Published by The Vanguard Press, New York, N. Y.

But, after all, the story belongs to him who tells it best, as Professor Brander T. Matthews of Columbia used to say, and in the version I heard there is no distortion of fact.

NUMBERS 36, 37.

The two ITALIAN stories I heard from Mr. Son,* a shoemaker on Broadway near where I live. He told me many stories with a merry twinkle in his eye. *Fools' Bells Ring in Every Town* and the Giufá tale are known and told in every land. They are different here in that they reflect the thoughts and attitude of Italian folk.

The Episode of the Rising of the Sun is also told in Portugal by Pedro da Malas Artes. Here he is a Smart-Aleck by the name of Peter. It is also known in Africa.

NUMBER 38.

I could not help but include at least one *Tyll Ulenspiegel* tale in the book. It shows that the scholars of Erfurt are about as fine a herd of Noodleheads as can be found anywhere.

Here the donkey plays an important part, as it so often does in folk tales.

NUMBER 39.

NORWAY has its Noodlehead hero in Silly Matt. His name is proverbial. Many stories are built around him and they follow the pattern found in other lands.

I heard the tale while in a bus traveling through Norway.

NUMBERS 40, 41.

GERMANY is full of tales of Noodleheads, and perhaps the most famous ones are about the citizens of Schilda. Many of

* See *The Priceless Cats,* published by The Vanguard Press, New York, N. Y.

these tales are almost identical with the Gotham escapades. I heard these stories when I lived in Austria.

Such tales were common all over Europe in the twelfth, thirteenth, and perhaps the fourteenth centuries, and were the important source of amusement and laughter. At least in comic tales there was a harmonious internationalism rather than a bristling hostile nationalism.

NUMBERS 42, 43, 44.

I heard many stories of Holmola, of FINLAND, when I was in Sweden, and they were told by men and women who were good folklorists and good storytellers. These tales are very popular in Finland, and they are popular in other lands in different versions.

NUMBERS 45, 46.

I heard these HUNGARIAN stories and many, many more when I was a youngster. My grandfather, for a few years, bred horses in Hungary—beautiful Arabian-bred horses, the kind that are famous all over Europe. We spent our summer vacations with him, and I heard many stories from the *csikós,* that is, the foreman, of the horse ranch. He had a very dark brown face full of wrinkles and wore wide trousers and a little felt hat with feathers in it. When he sat on his horse he looked like a king.

NUMBER 47.

I was born in AUSTRIA and remember a great many stories I heard and read there: Austrian tales and tales from other lands as well, even Cooper's Indian stories.

NUMBER 48.

When I was a youngster, my mother would get fish brought fresh from Galatz in RUMANIA. It was therefore fit and proper that I should hear "fish" stories from Rumania.

Tandala and Pakala are almost proverbial in that country, and many comic and trick tales are built around them. This is one of many I know.

NUMBER 49.

In SWITZERLAND, as in every land, the church played a most important part in folk life, and the church has always been an important theme in stories. Ghost stories, robber stories, all kinds of stories, including Noodlehead stories, center around the house of the Lord.

Widening the church, pushing it to another spot, is a theme often used. There is an Italian story of the Men of Montieri* who tried to *widen* their church.

I heard this Swiss story told in 1954 in Stockholm at a gathering of folklorists. I then heard it again when I traveled through Switzerland that very fall.

NUMBER 50.

The story of *Lutonya* is well known in RUSSIA and is the type that is known all over the world. I have known this particular story ever since childhood.

NUMBERS 51, 52.

I have often been to YUGOSLAVIA, and I have a host of friends in that country who have told me many tales. Mr.

* See *The Priceless Cats and Other Italian Folk Stories,* published by The Vanguard Press, New York, N. Y.

Blagoje Lazic, a Yugoslavian newspaperman now at the U.N., and Mr. Blanco Novakovic, acting head of the Yugoslavian Information Bureau in New York, both told me many tales of their country, and I had space to include just two: "The Tale of the Men of Prach," and "Smartness for Sale!"

NUMBER 53.

The little SPANISH story, "The Moon in the Donkey," is from the tales of Ludovicus Vives, an ancient scholar of Spain.

The reflection of the moon in ponds has always attracted olden peoples and is treated in many different ways. Often the yellow reflection of the moon is taken for cheese (as in the Gotham and other tales).

NUMBER 54.

In PORTUGAL there is a cycle of silly stories centered around a Noodlehead named Peter. The tales connected with him are common to Noodles throughout the world.

NUMBER 55.

I found the story of *The Wolf in the Sack* among my notes. Unfortunately, I either lost or mislaid the page on which there must have been a record of the one who told it to me and the place I heard it. I don't remember seeing it in print, but I am sure it is recorded somewhere. It is unquestionably of Eastern origin.

NUMBER 56.

The stories about Juan Bobo, are found not only in PUERTO RICO but in many South American countries and in the Caribbean Islands. New York City, with its very large population of Puerto Ricans, is a gold mine for tales of that island. It is there that I heard this story, and many others as well, about that Noodlehead, Juan Bobo.

NUMBER 57.

This type of CANADIAN-IRISH Noodlehead tale is well known throughout the world. In W. A. Clouston's book on Noodleheads there are many parallels to *Noodlehead Pat* showing that people enjoy a good laugh all over the world.

NUMBER 58.

Naturally, MEXICO has its city of Noodleheads. I heard *The Sombreros of the Men of Lagos* in a Mexican restaurant in New York City. This type of story is found in other lands.

NUMBERS 59, 60, 61, 62, 63, 64.

In the UNITED STATES there are not so many Noodle tales as are found in Europe, but here are a few that will hold their place with any.

NORTH AMERICAN INDIANS have Noodlehead tales just like the rest of the world. Among Apache Indians, Noddies are called "The Foolish People." Other tribes call them "The Spotted People." I heard these stories from an Apache Indian when I was in Arizona looking for comic Indian tales.

Professor M. E. Opler also heard these stories, and they were published in the *Memoirs of The American Folklore Society* (1942).

This type of story is found among many of the other North American Indian tribes and they have their parallels among European folk stories.